Dimensions Math®
Tests 4B

Singapore Math Inc.

Published by Singapore Math Inc.

19535 SW 129th Avenue
Tualatin, OR 97062
www.singaporemath.com

Dimensions Math® Tests 4B
ISBN 978-1-947226-54-8

First published 2020

Printed in China

Acknowledgments

Editing by the Singapore Math Inc. team.
Design and illustration by Cameron Wray with Carli Fronius.

Preface

Dimensions Math® Tests is a series of assessments to help teachers systematically evaluate student progress. The tests align with the content of Dimensions Math K–5 textbooks.

Dimensions Math Tests K uses pictorially engaging questions to test student ability to grasp key concepts through various methods including circling, matching, coloring, drawing, and writing numbers.

Dimensions Math Tests 1–5 have differentiated assessments. Tests consist of multiple-choice questions that assess comprehension of key concepts, and free response questions for students to demonstrate their problem-solving skills.

Test A focuses on key concepts and fundamental problem-solving skills.

Test B focuses on the application of analytical skills, thinking skills, and heuristics.

Contents

Chapter	Test	Page
Chapter 10 **Measurement**	Test A	1
	Test B	7
Chapter 11 **Area and Perimeter**	Test A	13
	Test B	19
Chapter 12 **Decimals**	Test A	25
	Test B	31
Chapter 13 **Addition and Subtraction of Decimals**	Test A	37
	Test B	43
	Continual Assessment 3 Test A	49
	Continual Assessment 3 Test B	57
Chapter 14 **Multiplication and Division of Decimals**	Test A	65
	Test B	71
Chapter 15 **Angles**	Test A	77
	Test B	83

Chapter	Test	Page
Chapter 16 **Lines and Shapes**	Test A	91
	Test B	99
Chapter 17 **Properties of Cuboids**	Test A	107
	Test B	113
	Year-end Assessment Test A	119
	Year-end Assessment Test B	131
Answer Key		143

BLANK

30 min | Score

Name: ______________________

Date: ______________________

40

Test A

Chapter 10 Measurement

Section A (2 points each)

Circle the correct option: **A**, **B**, **C**, or **D**.

1 2 L 700 mL + 2 L 630 mL = ______________

A 4 L 330 mL

B 70 mL

C 5 L 330 mL

D 3 L 330 mL

2 6 gal – 2 qt = [ ] qt

A 22

B 24

C 20

D 48

3. $1\frac{1}{3}$ h = ☐ min

A 20

B 70

C 80

D 90

4. What is 1 km 500 m ÷ 2?

A 1,500 m

B 750 m

C 300 m

D 750 km

5. 5 × 2 m 15 cm = ______________

A 2 m 75 cm

B 10 m 15 cm

C 2 m 25 cm

D 10 m 75 cm

Section B (2 points each)

6 105 min = ☐ h ☐ min

7 Express 80 cm as a fraction of 1 m.

8 Arrange the lengths in order from shortest to longest.

1 yd, $1\frac{1}{2}$ ft, 3ft 3 in, 35 in

______ ______ ______ ______

9 $3\frac{1}{5}$ cm = ☐ mm

10 Express 25 minutes as a fraction of $1\frac{1}{2}$ hours in simplest form.

11. A pumpkin weighs 3,340 g and a watermelon weighs 6 kg 300 g. How much heavier is the watermelon than the pumpkin? Express the answer in kilograms and grams.

12. A fence is $4\frac{5}{6}$ ft long. What is the length of the fence in inches?

13. A box of chocolate weighs 13 oz. How much do 3 boxes of chocolate weigh? Express the answer in pounds and ounces.

14. Mei filled an empty fish tank with 55 quarts of water. How much water did she pour into the fish tank? Express the answer in gallons and quarts.

Section C (4 points each)

15 What is the total weight of 2 bags of beans and 2 bags of rice? Express the answer in pounds and ounces.

16 David had 1 L 300 mL of orange juice. He used 800 mL of it and poured the rest equally into 2 glasses. How many milliliters of orange juice were there in each glass?

17 It took $1\frac{1}{4}$ h for a plane to fly from New York City to Philadelphia. The plane left New York City at 11:55 a.m. What time did it arrive in Philadelphia?

30 min

Score

Name: ______________________

Date: ______________________

/ 40

Test B

Chapter 10 Measurement

Section A (2 points each)

Circle the correct option: **A**, **B**, **C**, or **D**.

1 7 ft 8 in + 5 ft 6 in = ______________

A 12 ft 2 in

B 12 ft 4 in

C 13 ft 2 in

D 13 ft 4 in

2 20 min is a longer time than ______________.

A 20 h

B 360 s

C 4 h

D 1,200 s

3 How many inches are in 2 yd 2 ft?

A 48 **B** 74

C 60 **D** 96

4 $4\frac{3}{4}$ cup = ☐ fl oz

A 32 **B** 38

C 80 **D** 90

5 Which of the following is correct?

A $1\frac{1}{2}$ days < 12 h **B** 2 lb 4 oz = 38 oz

C $3\frac{3}{20}$ m = 315 cm **D** 2 yd 2 ft – 1 yd 1 ft = 1 ft

Section B (2 points each)

6. Arrange the following weights in order from heaviest to lightest.

1 kg 1 g, 1,100 g, $1\frac{1}{4}$ kg, 1 kg 50 g

________ ________ ________ ________

7. $3 \times \frac{4}{5}$ L = ☐ L ☐ mL

8. Express $15\frac{1}{3}$ min in minutes and seconds.

9. Express 12 h as a fraction of $2\frac{1}{2}$ days in simplest form.

10. Grace is 4 ft 4 in tall. Kenya is 8 in shorter than Grace. How tall is Kenya in feet and inches?

11 A pot can hold $2\frac{3}{4}$ gal of water. There are 7 pints of water in the pot. How many more pints of water can Megan pour in before the pot spills over?

12 Dion has a ribbon 3 m 15 cm long. He used 95 cm of the ribbon to tie a present. What is the length of the remaining ribbon? Express the answer in meters and centimeters.

13 A machine at a factory operates continuously from 5:00 a.m. on Monday until 6:00 p.m. on Friday every week. How many hours does the machine operate weekly without stopping?

14 Kona ran $1\frac{2}{5}$ km every day for 4 days. What is the total distance she ran in the 4 days in kilometers and meters?

Section C (4 points each)

15 Corey bought 3 lb 9 oz of white beans, 15 oz of black beans, and $2\frac{1}{8}$ lb of red beans. How many pounds and ounces of beans did he buy altogether?

16 Macy arrived at a train station at 10:25 a.m. She boarded her train at 11:20 a.m. The train left the station $\frac{1}{4}$ h after she boarded. How many hours was Macy at the train station before her train left? Express the answer as a mixed number in simplest form.

 A pumpkin is 1 kg 30 g heavier than a watermelon. The watermelon is three times heavier than a papaya. The papaya weighs 707 g. What is the weight of the pumpkin? Express the answer in kilograms and grams.

25 min Score

Name: ______________________

Date: ______________________

30

Test A

Chapter 11 Area and Perimeter

Section A (2 points each)

Circle the correct option: **A**, **B**, **C**, or **D**.

1 The area of the square is _______ ft^2.

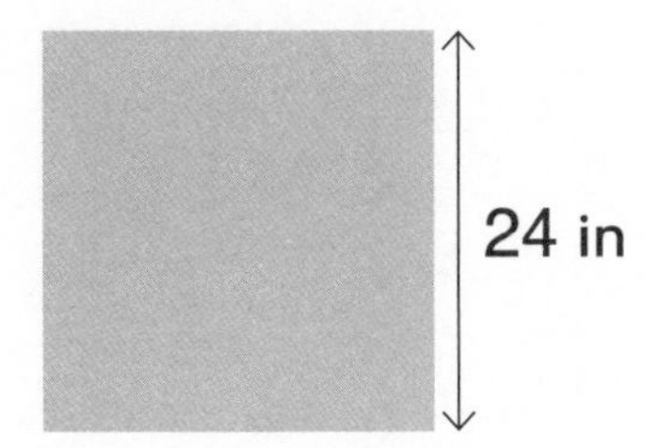

A 8 **B** 4

C 576 **D** 48

2 What is the area of this rectangle in square centimeters?

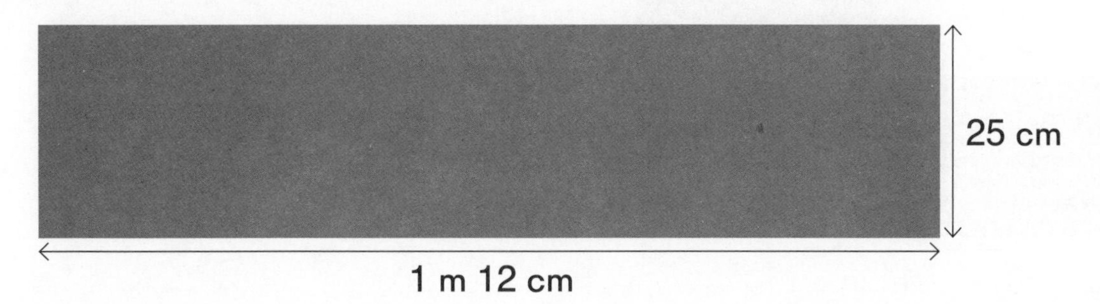

A 2,550 cm^2 **B** 280 cm^2

C 2,800 cm^2 **D** 137 cm^2

3 A square has a perimeter of 124 cm. What is the length of one side of the square?

A 31 cm

B 62 cm

C 248 cm

D 448 cm

4 The area of this rectangle is 192 m^2. What is the unknown length?

A 87 m

B 48 m

C 184 m

D 24 m

5 What is the perimeter of this figure?

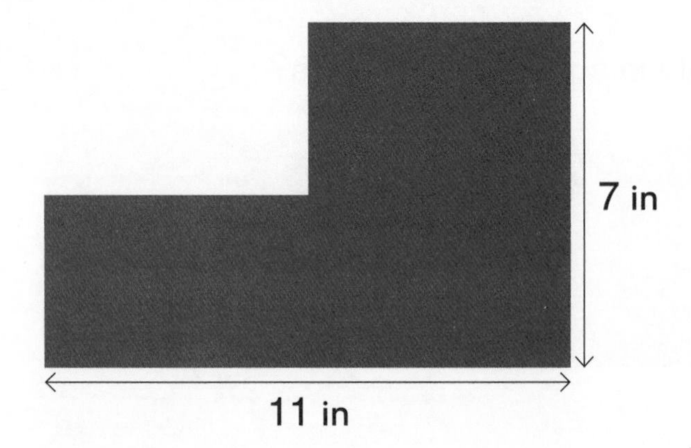

A 18 in

B 77 in

C 36 in

D 29 in

Section B (2 points each)

6 The perimeter of this rectangle is 4 m. What is its width in centimeters?

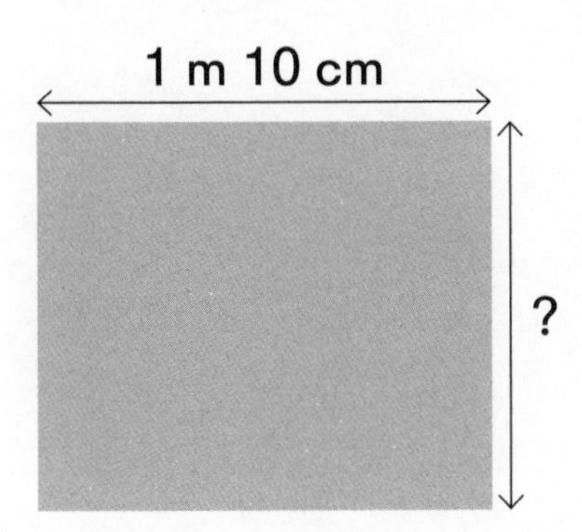

7 Find the length of the rectangle. Express the answer in feet.

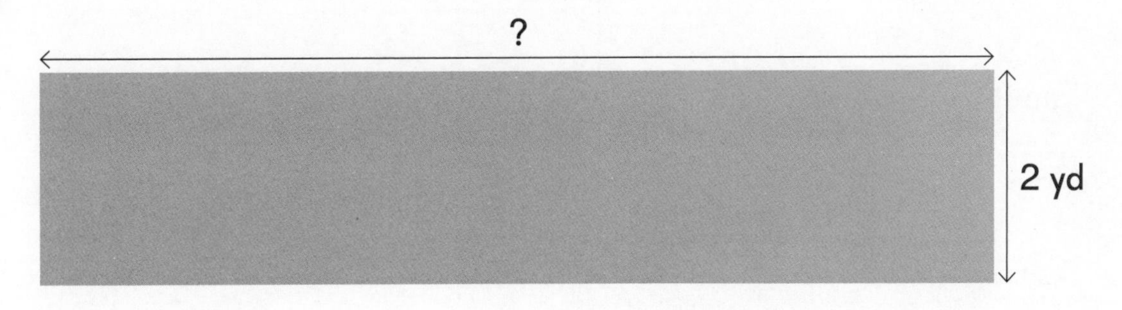

Area = 168 ft^2

8. Find the area of this square. Express the answer in square feet.

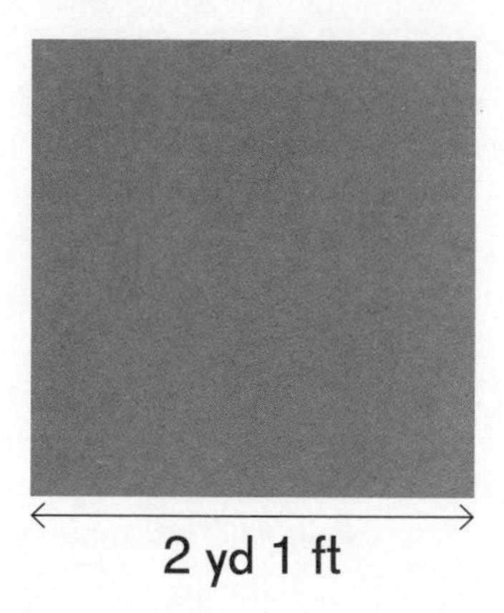

9. Find the area of the shaded part of the rectangle.

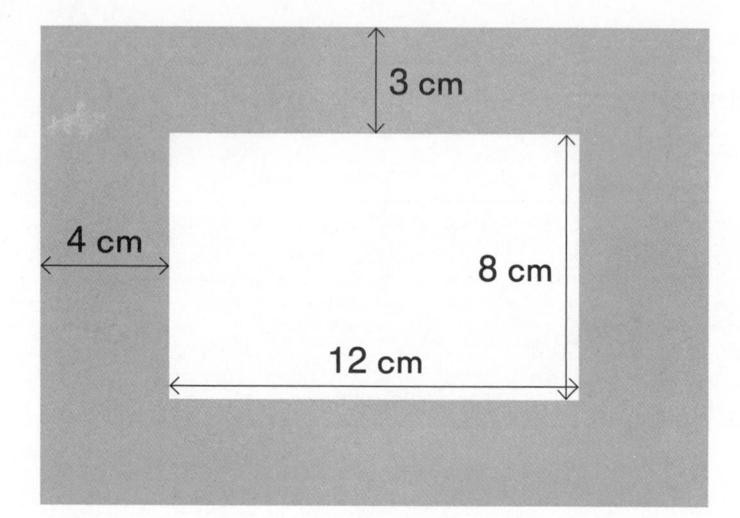

10 Find the perimeter of this figure.

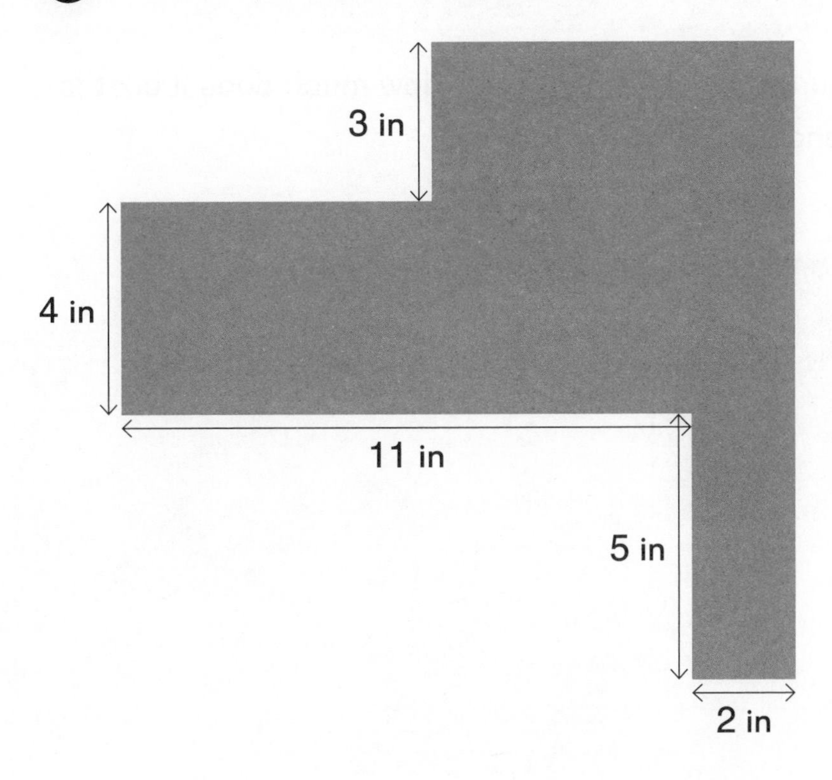

11 Find the perimeter of this figure.

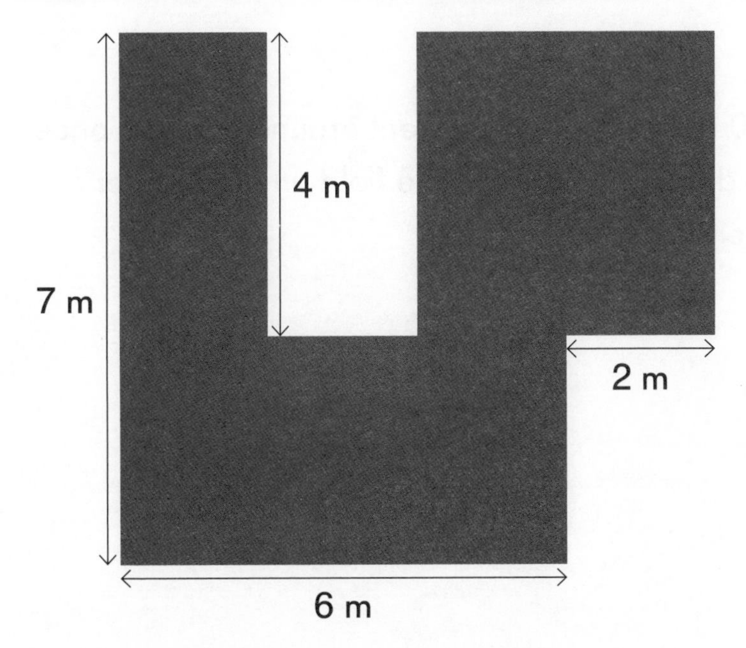

Section C (4 points each)

12 A rectangular field measures 30 yd 2 ft by 15 yd. How much does it cost to fence the field if 1 ft of fence costs $3?

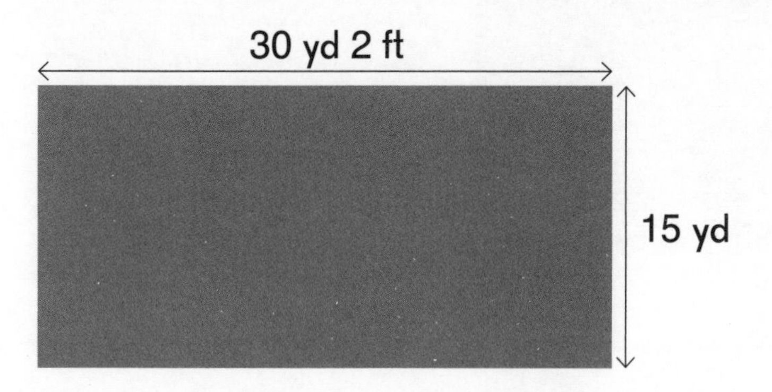

13 A rectangular field is 1 km 500 m by 450 m. Alex went around the field once on his scooter. What distance did he ride around the field on his scooter? Express the answer in kilometers and meters.

25 min　Score

Name: ______________________

Date: ______________________

30

Test B

Chapter 11 Area and Perimeter

Section A (2 points each)

Circle the correct option: **A**, **B**, **C**, or **D**.

1 The area of the rectangle is ____________ square centimeters.

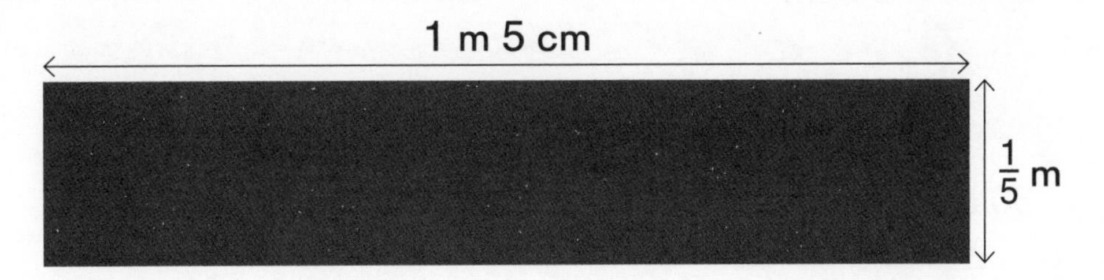

A 2,100　　**B** 3,000

C 2,625　　**D** 250

2 The area of the rectangle is 18 in². What is the unknown length in inches?

A $\frac{1}{4}$ in　　**B** 3 in

C 6 in　　**D** $\frac{1}{2}$ in

3 A square has a perimeter of 2 yd 2 ft. What is the length of one side in feet?

A 4 ft

B 2 ft

C 1 ft

D 3 ft

4 What is the area of the shaded part of this rectangle?

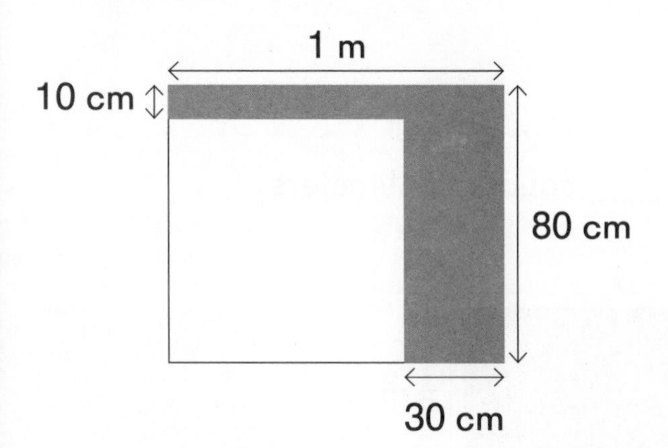

A 310 cm²

B 3,100 cm²

C 490 cm²

D 8,000 cm²

5 What is the perimeter of this figure?

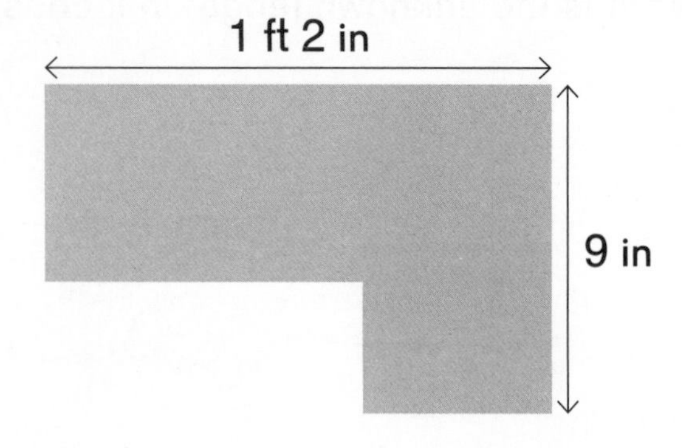

A 42 in

B 23 in

C 46 in

D 2 ft 4 in

Section B (2 points each)

6. A square has an area of 81 cm^2. What is its perimeter?

7. Find the unknown side. Express the answer in yards.

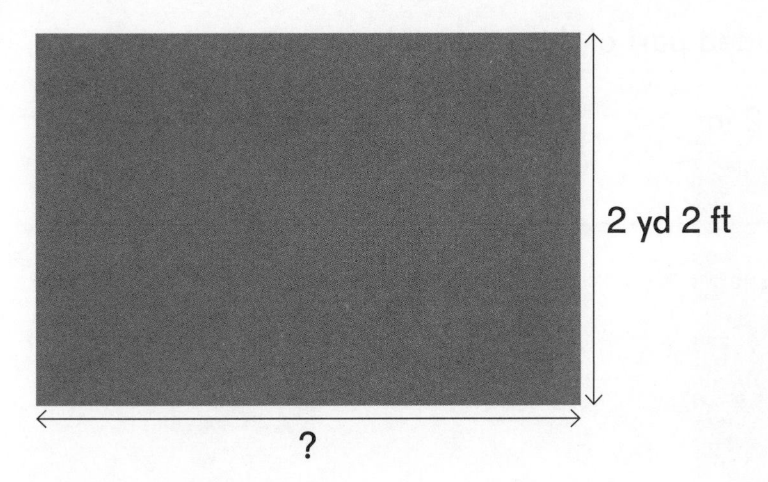

Area = 96 ft^2

8 Find the perimeter of this figure.

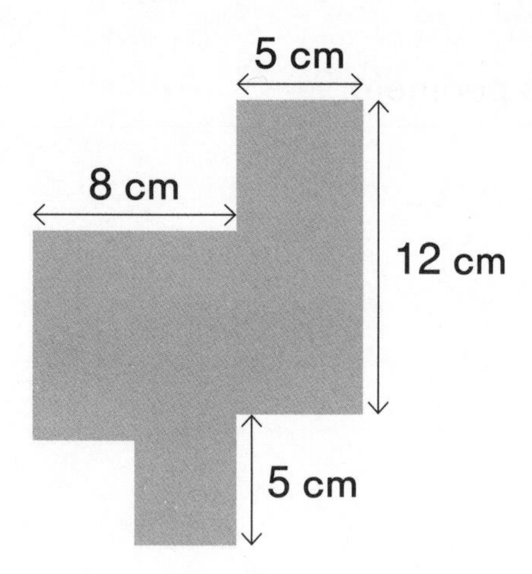

9 Find the area of the shaded part of this rectangle.

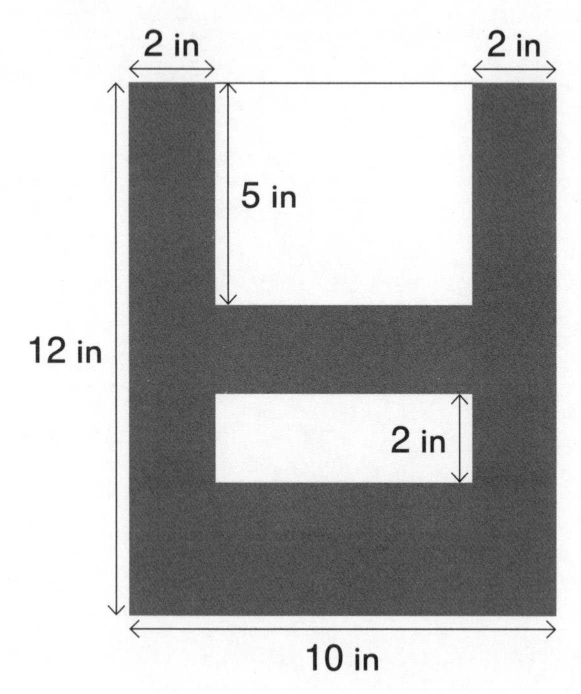

10 Find the perimeter of this figure.

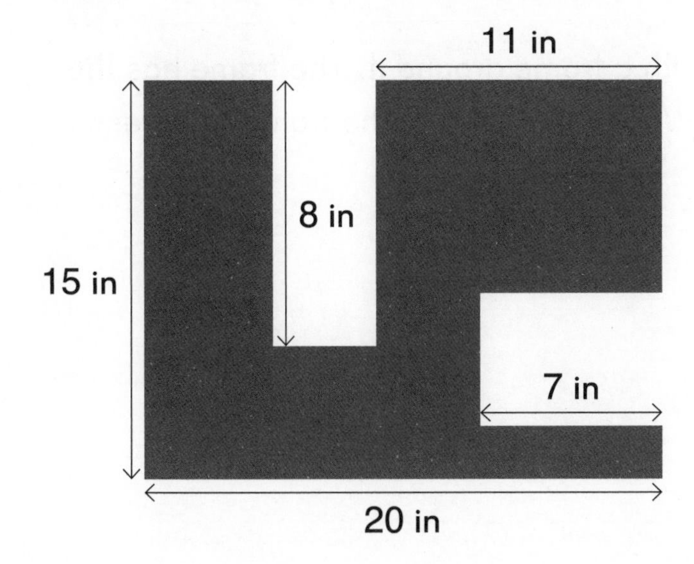

11 A rectangle has a perimeter of 5 m 50 cm. Its width is 80 cm. What is its length in meters and centimeters?

Section C (4 points each)

12 The figure shows a square picture with a frame around it. The frame has the same width all around the picture. What is the area of the frame? Express the answer in square inches.

13 How much will it cost Hunter to put a fence around this plot of land if 1 m of fence costs $4?

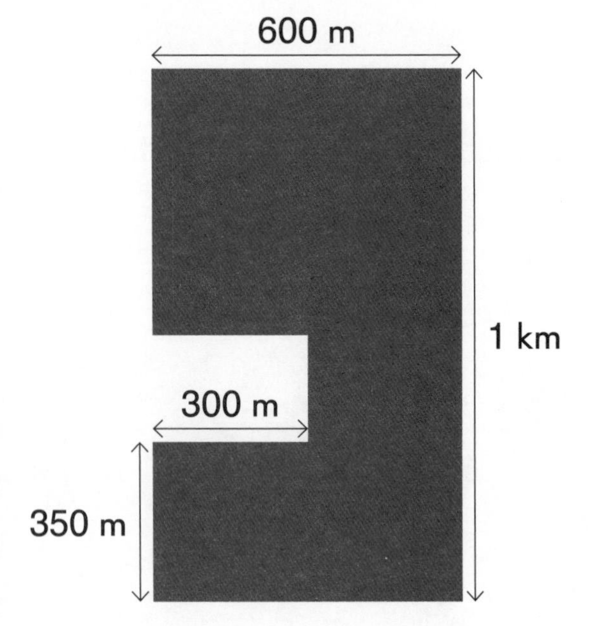

25 min Score

Name: ____________________

Date: ____________________

40

Test A

Chapter 12 Decimals

Section A (2 points each)

Circle the correct option: **A**, **B**, **C**, or **D**.

1 Which digit is in the tenths place in 21.83?

A 1 **B** 8

C 0 **D** 3

2 What number is 0.1 more than 34.56?

A 34.57 **B** 35.56

C 44.56 **D** 34.66

3. Which of the following is the least number?

A 0.99

B 1

C 0.3

D 3.1

4. What is 4.48 lb rounded to the nearest whole number of pounds?

A 4.5 lb

B 5 lb

C 4 lb

D 4.4 lb

5. Which of the following is equal in length to 12 cm?

A 1.2 m

B 0.12 m

C 12 m

D 120 m

Section B (2 points each)

6. Write $3\frac{1}{10}$ as a decimal.

7. What is 10.78 rounded to 1 decimal place?

8. Complete the number pattern.

12.8		13	13.1		

9. 10 + 0.1 + 0.03 = ☐

10 7 + ☐ + 0.05 = 7.25

11 6.54 − 0.5 = ☐

12 Write the decimal indicated by the arrow.

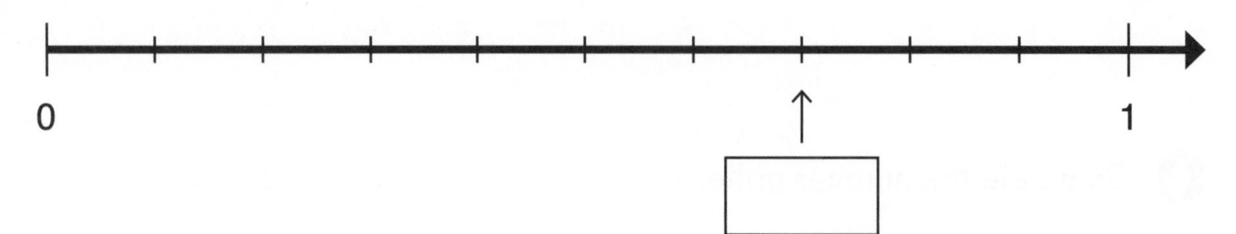

13 Write the length of the paperclip in centimeters as a decimal.

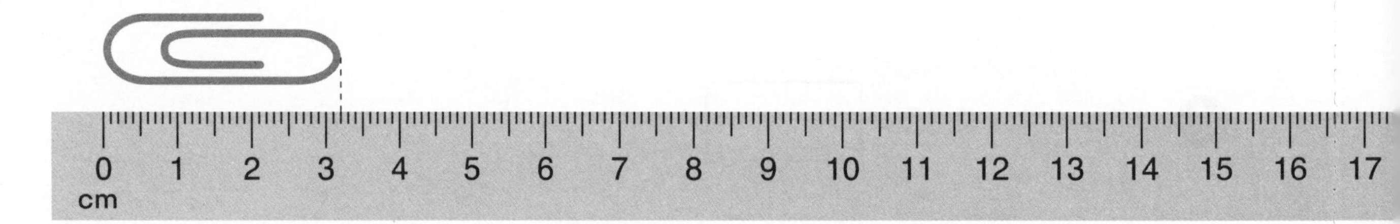

14 Circle the values that are the same as nine tenths.

9.0	$\frac{9}{10}$	90	10.9	0.9

15 Express 1 ten + 2 ones + 3 tenths + 4 hundredths as a decimal.

16 Express 0.12 as a fraction in simplest form.

17 The length of a rope is 1.58 m. Round the length to one decimal place.

18 Write the numbers in increasing order.

15.12, 15.05, 15.27, $15\frac{1}{4}$

______ ______ ______ ______

19 Sandy spent $28.30 at the market. Round the amount she spent to the nearest dollar.

20 A piece of string is 1.45 m long. Express the length in meters as a mixed number in simplest form.

25 min | Score: ___ / 40

Name: ______________________

Date: ______________________

Test B

Chapter 12 Decimals

Section A (2 points each)
Circle the correct option: **A**, **B**, **C**, or **D**.

1 In which number is the digit 5 in the tenths place?

A 57.61 **B** 87.05

C 95.87 **D** 28.52

2 What number is 1 tenth less than 83.12?

A 73.12 **B** 82.12

C 83.02 **D** 83.11

3 What is the value of the digit 4 in 1.94?

A 4 tens

B 4 hundredths

C 4 ones

D 4 tenths

4 Which one of the following is equal to $\frac{3}{25}$?

A 3.25

B 0.3

C 0.12

D 0.15

5 $9\frac{11}{20} = \square$

A 9.11

B 9.55

C 9.20

D 9.5

Section B (2 points each)

6 Write the decimal indicated by the arrow.

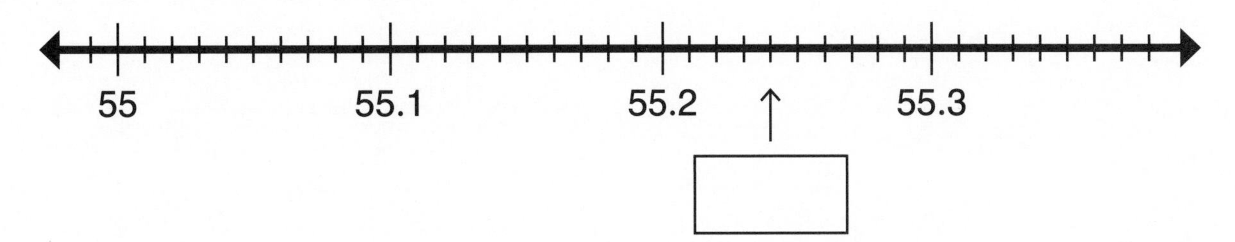

7 Write 41.07 in expanded form.

8 Complete the number pattern.

5.14	5.12		5.08		

9 60 + 7 + 0.9 + 0.01 = ☐

10. $\square + 0.2 + 20 = 20.28$

11. $581.04 - 80 = \square$

12. Express 3 hundreds + 1 ten + 5 hundredths as a decimal.

13. Write >, <, or = in the ◯.

    7.07 ◯ 7.7

14 Express the following length as a decimal.

3 cm = ☐ m

15 Express $\frac{9}{4}$ as a decimal.

16 Express 50.6 as a mixed number in simplest form.

17 Write the numbers in decreasing order.

2.3, $3\frac{3}{4}$, $2\frac{5}{10}$, 3.7

______ ______ ______ ______

18 A sack of rice weighs 10.75 kg.

(a) Express the weight in kilograms as a mixed number in simplest form.

(b) Express the weight in kilograms and grams.

19 Kale ran a mile in 9.58 min.

(a) Express his time to the nearest tenth of a minute.

(b) Express his time to the nearest minute.

20 A pole is 1 meter long. $\frac{1}{5}$ of the pole is painted green. The rest of the pole is unpainted. What part of the pole is unpainted? Express the answer in meters as a decimal.

30 min Score

Name: ______________________

Date: ______________________

/ 40

Test A

Chapter 13 Addition and Subtraction of Decimals

Section A (2 points each)

Circle the correct option: **A**, **B**, **C**, or **D**.

1 0.3 + 0.6 = ☐

A 0.9 **B** 3.6

C 0.3 **D** 0.36

2 18 tenths – 4 tenths = ______

A 140 **B** 14

C 0.14 **D** 1.4

3 $13.6 + 8.44 = \square$

A 21.04 **B** 22.04

C 5.16 **D** 2.24

4 What is 9.6 lb more than 35.8 lb?

A 454 lb **B** 26.2 lb

C 45.4 lb **D** 36.76 lb

5 What is $0.12 less than $0.89?

A $8.78 **B** $7.70

C $0.77 **D** $1.01

Section B (2 points each)

6 $0.03 + 0.04 = \square$

7 $0.7 + \square = 1.6$

8 What fraction of $1 is 40¢?

9 Add 6.76 and 7.92.

10 Write >, <, or = in the ◯.

$0.1 - 0.05 \bigcirc 0.02 \times 2$

11. Subtract 6.27 from 15.

12. A basket of carrots weighs 7.29 kg. The empty basket weighs 0.58 kg. How much do the carrots weigh?

13. Package A weighs 2.3 kg. Package B weighs 4.2 kg. Package C weighs 3.1 kg. What is the difference in weight between the heaviest and the lightest package in kilograms?

14. An empty tank has a capacity of 12 gal. Alex pours 1.7 gal of water into the tank. How many more gallons of water can be added for the tank to be full?

Section C (2 points each)

15 Han had 1 L of milk. He used 0.5 L of the milk to make some pies and $\frac{1}{4}$ L to make gravy. How many liters of milk were left? Express the answer as a decimal.

16 Kate bought 1.27 lb of red peppers, 0.85 lb of green peppers, and 2.51 lb of yellow peppers. How many pounds of peppers did she buy?

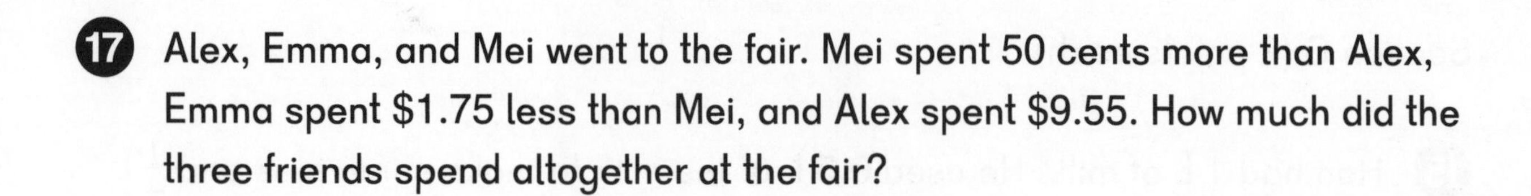

17. Alex, Emma, and Mei went to the fair. Mei spent 50 cents more than Alex, Emma spent \$1.75 less than Mei, and Alex spent \$9.55. How much did the three friends spend altogether at the fair?

30 min Score

Name: ______________________

Date: ______________________

/40

Test B

Chapter 13 Addition and Subtraction of Decimals

Section A (2 points each)

Circle the correct option: **A**, **B**, **C**, or **D**.

1. 0.5 + 0.5 = ☐

A 0.55 **B** 1

C 10 **D** 5.5

2. 1 one 4 tenths – 6 tenths = ☐

A 0.8 **B** 8

C 1.6 **D** 0.4

3 $4.2 + 5.8 + 3.72 = \square$

A 13.2

B 1.37

C 12.72

D 13.72

4 What is 5.8 less than 36?

A 3.2

B 41.8

C 30.2

D 35.42

5 What is the sum of 0.75 and 0.3?

A 0.78

B 1.05

C 3.75

D 0.45

Section B (2 points each)

6. $0.04 + \square = 0.05$

7. $1 - 0.99 = \square$

8. Subtract 4.67 from 13.7.

9. Add 0.78 and 9.95.

10. Complete the number pattern.

11.8	11.64		11.32		

11 Write >, <, or = in the ◯.

$\frac{1}{20} + 72.83$ ◯ $83.03 - 4\frac{3}{4}$

12 Dion took 1.4 min to run around a field once. Alex took 0.08 min less than Dion to run around the same field once. How long did it take Alex to run around the field once? Express the answer in minutes as a decimal.

13 Three pumpkins weigh 1.4 kg, $7\frac{2}{5}$ kg, and 0.51 kg. What is the total weight of the pumpkins in kilograms? Express the answer as a decimal.

14 Ashlee had \$5. She spent \$4.20. What fraction of \$5 does she have left? Express the answer in simplest form.

Section C (2 points each)

15. A birdhouse kit costs \$3.66 less than a dream catcher kit. The dream catcher kit costs \$17.15 more than a pack of cards. The pack of cards costs \$0.89. How much does the birdhouse kit cost?

16. The length of a rectangle is 0.75 m and its width is $\frac{1}{2}$ m. Find the perimeter of this rectangle in meters. Express the answer as a decimal.

17 The park, the library, the post office, and the school are on the same road. The distances from the library to the park and from the library to the post office are the same. What is the distance between the post office and the school?

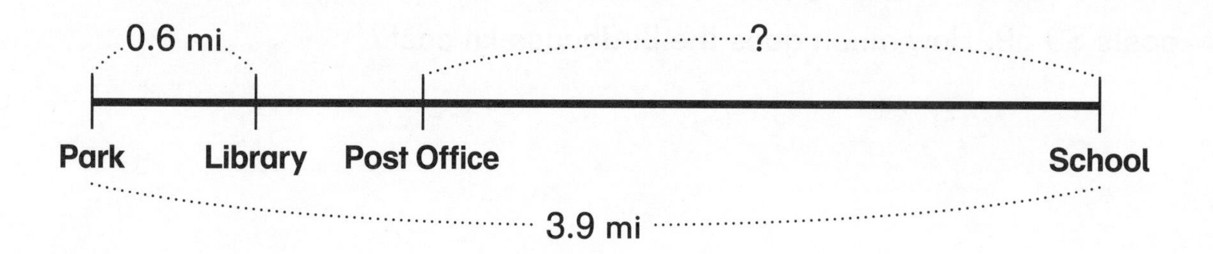

45 min Score

Name: ______________________

Date: ______________________

60

Test A

Continual Assessment 3

Section A (2 points each)

Circle the correct option: **A**, **B**, **C**, or **D**.

1 Which of the following is a common factor of 28 and 42?

A 4 **B** 7

C 6 **D** 28

2 What does the digit 8 stand for in 537.81?

A 80 tenths **B** 8 hundredths

C 8 tenths **D** 80 ones

3 $\frac{3}{4}$ qt = ☐ c

A 3 **B** 34

C 7 **D** 12

4 6 ft 6 in – 10 in = ☐

A 5 ft 10 in

B 6 ft 8 in

C 5 ft 8 in

D 7 ft 4 in

5 5 cm = ☐ m

A $\frac{1}{2}$

B $\frac{1}{20}$

C 50

D $\frac{1}{5}$

6 The perimeter of the rectangle is 50 cm. What is the unknown length?

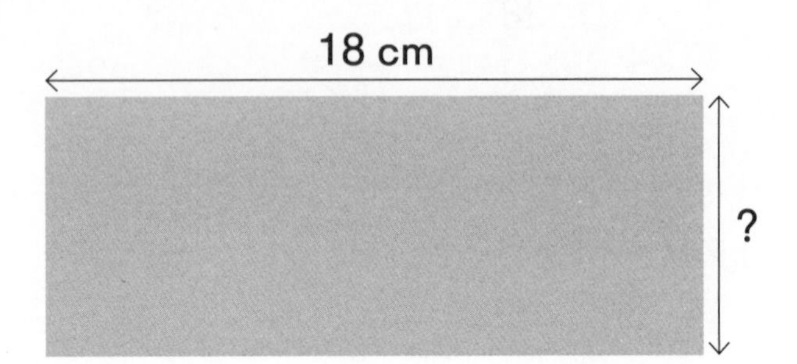

A 14 cm

B 16 cm

C 25 cm

D 7 cm

7 2 ones + 5 tenths = ☐

A 25

B 2.05

C 2.5

D 21.5

8 What is the decimal indicated by the arrow?

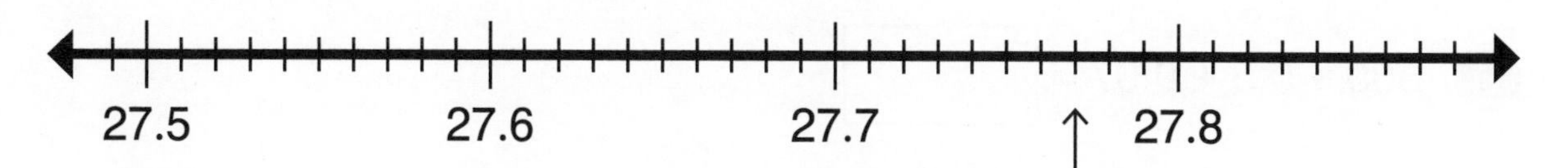

A 27.7 **B** 27.77

C 27.07 **D** 27.87

9 What number is 0.01 more than 0.3?

A 0.31 **B** 0.29

C 0.4 **D** 0.13

10 Which one of the following numbers is 3.9 when rounded to 1 decimal place?

A 3.8 **B** 3.08

C 3.85 **D** 4

Section B (2 points each)

11 $500 + 0.5 + 0.07 =$ ☐

12 Express 30 min as a fraction of 3 hours in simplest form.

13 Express the area of the rectangle in square feet.

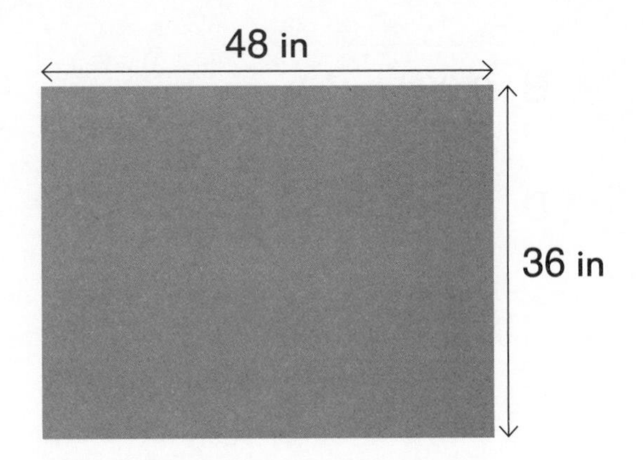

14 Complete the number pattern.

97.04	97.06		97.1		

15 Express 3 tenths 8 hundredths as a decimal.

16 7.24 − 0.55 = ☐

17 Mary had a piece of string 13 ft long. She used 4 ft 5 in of it to tie a package. What is the length of the string left? Express the answer in feet and inches.

18 Find the perimeter of this figure in inches.

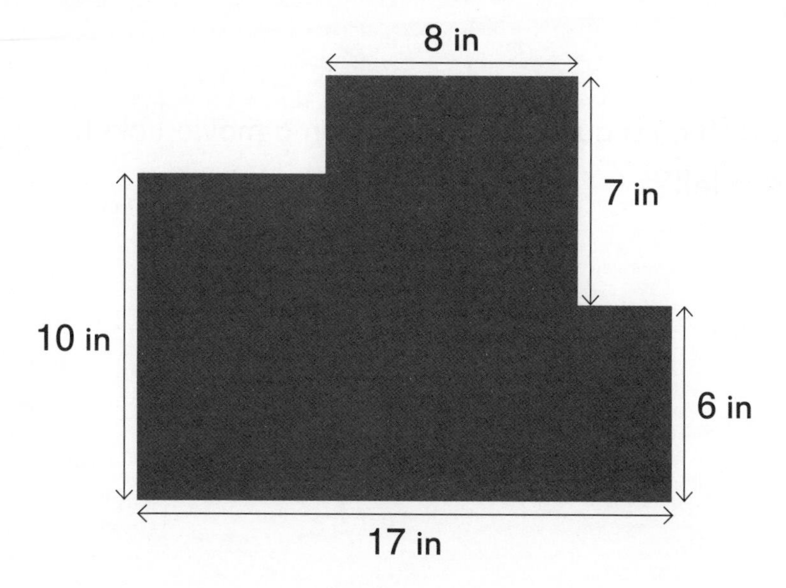

19 What is the area of the shaded part of this figure?

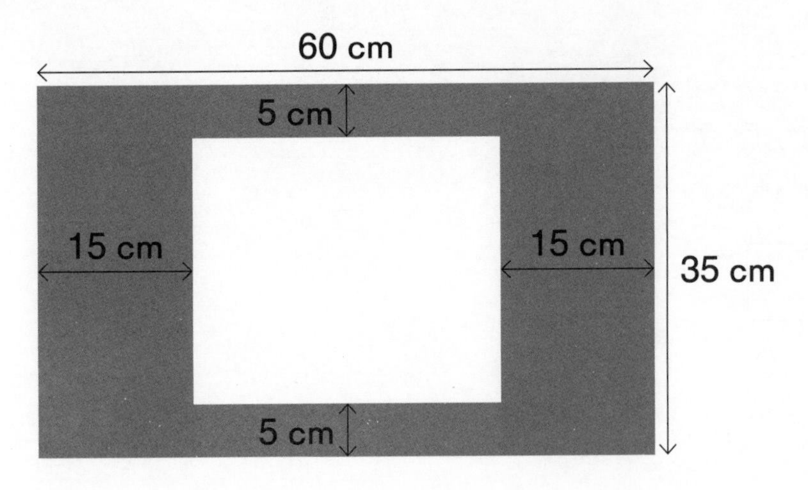

20 John had $36.25. He spent $1.75 on a bus ticket and $7 on a movie ticket. How much money does he have left?

Section C (4 points each)

21 Alex arrived for his swimming lesson 5 min early. His lesson was $1\frac{1}{4}$ h long. He finished at 1:00 p.m. What time did he arrive for his lesson?

22 Harry had 5 lb of flour. He used 2 lb 6 oz of it to bake some cakes and put equal amounts of the rest in two containers. How much flour did he put in each container? Express the answer in pounds and ounces.

23. A rectangular garden has a width of $3\frac{2}{3}$ yd. The length of the garden is twice that of its width. What is the area of this garden in square feet?

24. A notebook costs twice as much as a ruler. A pen costs 35 cents less than the notebook. The ruler costs $1.15. How much does the pen cost?

25. Jenna had 3.25 L of milk. She used $\frac{1}{2}$ L to make a pudding and 1.3 L to make milkshakes. How much milk does she have left?

45 min Score

/ 60

Name: ____________________

Date: ____________________

Test B

Continual Assessment 3

Section A (2 points each)

Circle the correct option: **A**, **B**, **C**, or **D**.

1. What is the eighth multiple of 6?

   A 36 **B** 14

   C 48 **D** 64

2. What is 51,863 rounded to the nearest ten thousand?

   A 50,000 **B** 51,000

   C 52,000 **D** 51,870

3. 3 c 4 fl oz = ☐ fl oz

   A 24 **B** 27

   C 28 **D** 12

4 $\frac{3}{4}$ lb − 2 oz = ☐ oz

A 14

B 10

C 1

D 12

5 $1\frac{7}{12}$ days = ______

A 14 h

B 38 min

C 38 h

D 95 h

6 What is the unknown length in yards?

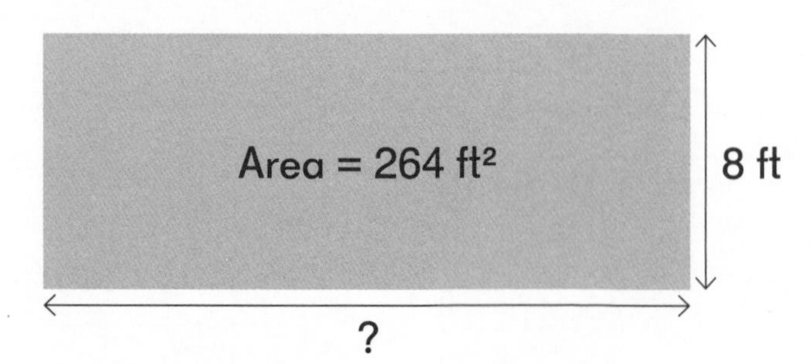

A 33 yd

B 11 yd

C 99 yd

D 124 yd

7 What is 0.04 as a fraction in simplest form?

A $\frac{1}{50}$

B $\frac{2}{5}$

C $\frac{2}{25}$

D $\frac{1}{25}$

8 1 one 3 tenths − 9 tenths = ______

A 0.4

B 4

C 40

D 2.2

9 What is 16.45 seconds rounded to the nearest second?

A 17 s

B 16 s

C 16.5 s

D 16.4 s

10 Which of the following has the greatest value?

A 0.25

B $\frac{1}{20}$

C 2 tenths 2 hundredths

D 0.1 + 0.16

Section B (2 points each)

11. Write 715.43 in expanded form.

12. Express 50 cm as a fraction of $1\frac{1}{2}$ m in simplest form.

13. Express the area of this rectangle in square inches.

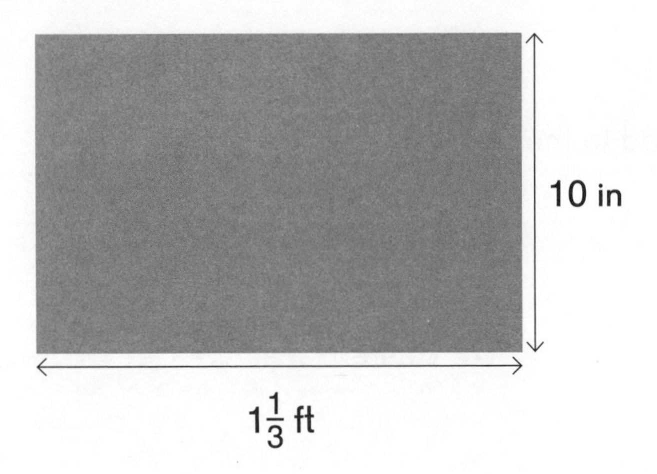

14. Arrange the numbers in order from least to greatest.

$\frac{2}{5}$, 0.04, $1\frac{1}{4}$, 1.2

______ ______ ______ ______

15 Express 6 ones 6 hundredths as a decimal.

16 $12 - 0.08 = \square$

17 A plank is 2 m 60 cm long. What is the total length of 2 such planks? Express the answer in meters and centimeters.

18 Find the perimeter of this figure.

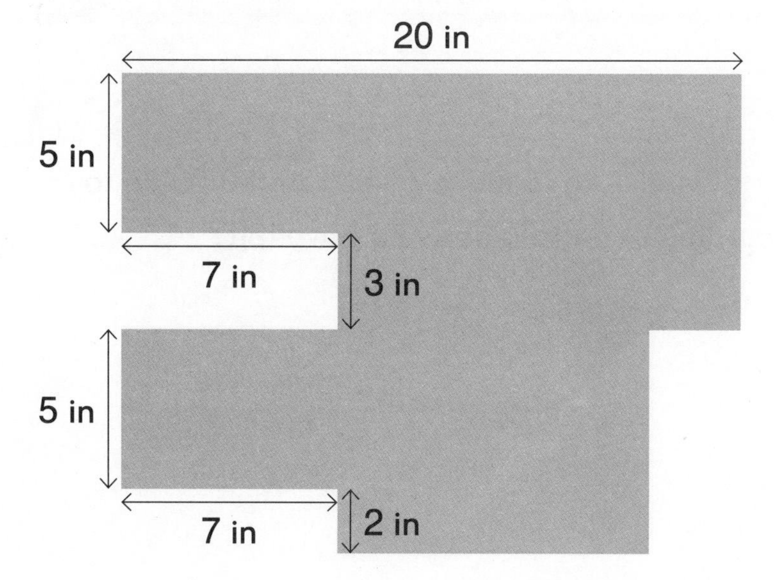

19 Find the area of the shaded part of the rectangle in square centimeters.

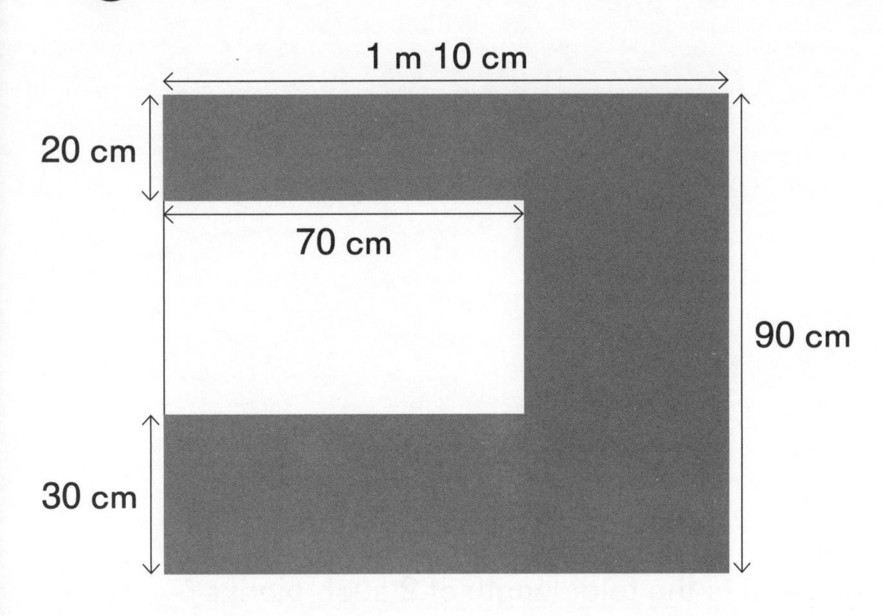

20 John bought 2 kg of carrots. He used 1 kg to make a soup and 0.53 kg to make a salad. How many kilograms of carrots does he have left?

Section C (4 points each)

21 A pineapple weighs twice as much a papaya. A grapefruit weighs 5 oz less than the papaya. The total weight of these fruits is 3 lb 3 oz. What is the weight of the pineapple in pounds and ounces?

22 Emma arrived 10 minutes before school started at 7:35 a.m. She stayed $\frac{3}{4}$ h for choir practice after school ended at 2:10 p.m. How much time did Emma spend at school? Express the answer in hours and minutes.

23. A rectangular door and a square window at a museum have the same perimeter. The length of the door is three times its width. The area of the window is 36 ft^2. What is the area of the door?

24. A pitcher can hold 0.85 L of water, a kettle has twice the capacity of the pitcher, and a pot can hold $1\frac{1}{10}$ L of water. What is the total capacity of the three containers in liters? Express the answer as a decimal.

25. Hannah bought 26 boxes of chocolate. Each box contains $\frac{3}{8}$ lb of chocolate. How many pounds of chocolate did Hannah buy? Express the answer as a decimal.

35 min Score

Name: ______________________

Date: ______________________

/40

Test A

Chapter 14 Multiplication and Division of Decimals

Section A (2 points each)

Circle the correct option: **A**, **B**, **C**, or **D**.

1 $0.03 \times 2 = \square$

A 0.6 **B** 0.23

C 0.06 **D** 6

2 5 tenths $\times 7 = \square$

A 0.35 **B** 350

C 35 **D** 3.5

3. $0.8 \div 8 = \square$

A 1.0

B 0.1

C 6.4

D 0.01

4. A picture is 9 cm by 7.17 cm. What is its area?

A 64.53 cm^2

B 63.93 cm^2

C 16.17 cm^2

D 32.34 cm^2

5. Two identical bicycles cost $346.80. How much does one bicycle cost?

A $693.60

B $173.40

C $123.40

D $115.60

Section B (2 points each)

6. $0.05 \times 5 = \square$

7. $0.24 \div 4 = \square$

8. Divide 240.24 by 6.

9. Find the product of 123.2 and 5.

10. Write > or < in the ◯. Use estimation.

$7.3 \times 5 \bigcirc 3.8 \times 7$

11 Circle the numbers that are less than $4.6 \div 4$.

2	1.05	1.2	1.12

12 A bag of beans weighs 0.5 kg. What is the weight of 4 bags of beans in kilograms?

13 4 friends paid $35 to play miniature golf and they shared the cost equally. How much did each friend pay?

14 The length of the rectangular field is 3 times its width. The width of the field is 0.76 km. What is the length of the field in kilometers?

Section C (2 points each)

15. 6 cupcakes cost \$3.60. How much do 8 cupcakes cost?

16. June had 1 L of juice. She used 0.3 L of it and poured the rest of the juice equally into 5 glasses. How many liters of juice is in each glass? Express the answer in decimals.

2 adult train tickets and 1 child train ticket cost a total of $228.05. 1 child ticket costs $45.40 less than 1 adult ticket. How much does 1 adult ticket cost?

35 min Score

Name: ______________________

Date: ______________________

Score
40

Test B

Chapter 14 Multiplication and Division of Decimals

Section A (2 points each)

Circle the correct option: **A**, **B**, **C**, or **D**.

1. $0.01 \times 1 =$ ☐

   A 0.11 **B** 1

   C 1.1 **D** 0.01

2. 7 tenths × 2 = ☐ hundredths

   A 14 **B** 140

   C 1.4 **D** 0.14

3 A square has a perimeter of 15.04 cm. What is the length of one side?

A 3.76 cm

B 7.02 cm

C 3.7 cm

D 7.52 cm

4 A rectangular field is 51.86 km by 8 km. What is its area?

A 6.5 km^2

B 414.48 km^2

C 414.88 km^2

D 119.72 km^2

5 564.4 ÷ 8 = ☐

A 70.5

B 70.55

C 7.5

D 70.6

Section B (2 points each)

6. $0.09 \times 9 = \square$

7. $0.4 \div 5 = \square$

8. Find the product of 401.8 and 5.

9. Divide 0.63 by 7.

10. Write > or < in the ◯. Use estimation.

$5.4 \times 2 \bigcirc 78.4 \div 8$

11. Circle the number that $12.6 \div 4$ is closest to.

31	3.4	3.2	3.05

12. One rock painting kit costs $25.50. How much do 4 kits cost?

13. The capacity of a bucket is 8 times that of a bottle. The bottle can hold 0.9 L of water. What is the capacity of the bucket in liters?

14. Ali biked the same distance each day for 8 days. He biked 54 miles altogether in the 8 days. How many miles did he bike each day?

Section C (2 points each)

15. Laila used 4 bags of chocolate chips to make 8 cakes. Each bag of chocolate chips weighed 2.5 kg. How many kilograms of chocolate chips did she use to make each cake?

16. 6 pencils cost $6.90 and 3 erasers cost $1.20. Pablo bought 8 pencils and 5 erasers. How much did he spend altogether?

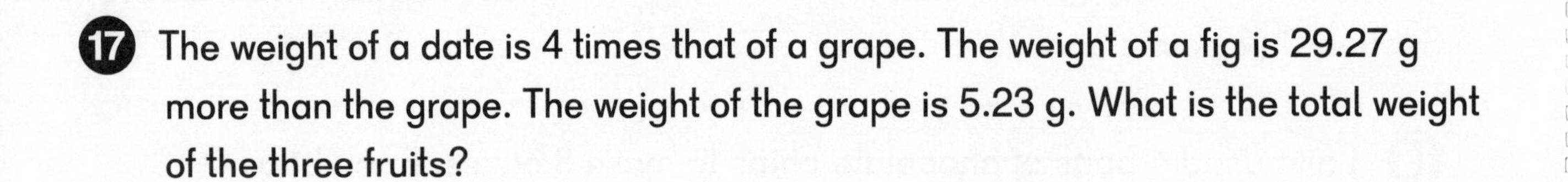

17 The weight of a date is 4 times that of a grape. The weight of a fig is 29.27 g more than the grape. The weight of the grape is 5.23 g. What is the total weight of the three fruits?

Name: ____________________

Date: ____________________

25 min

Score

30

Test A

Chapter 15 Angles

Section A (2 points each)

Circle the correct option: **A**, **B**, **C**, or **D**.

You will need a set square, a protractor, and a ruler for this test.

1 $\frac{1}{4}$ turn = ______

A 180° **B** 90°

C 0° **D** 360°

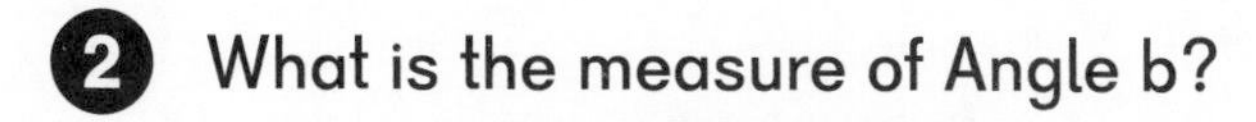

2 What is the measure of Angle b?

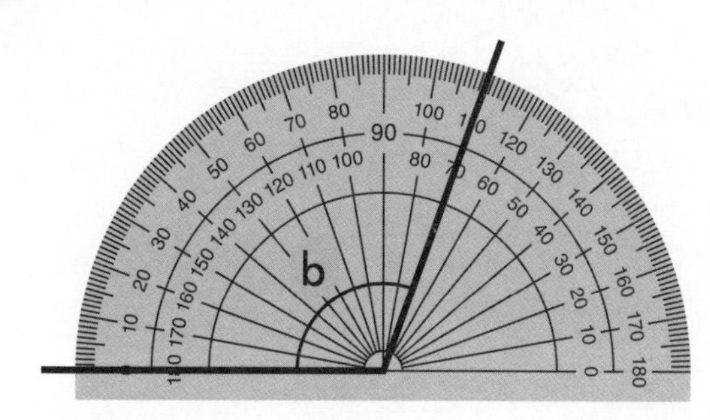

A 70° **B** 120°

C 110° **D** 80°

3 Which of the following is a measure of an acute angle?

A 55° **B** 210°

C 91° **D** 135°

4 Which angle measures 105°?

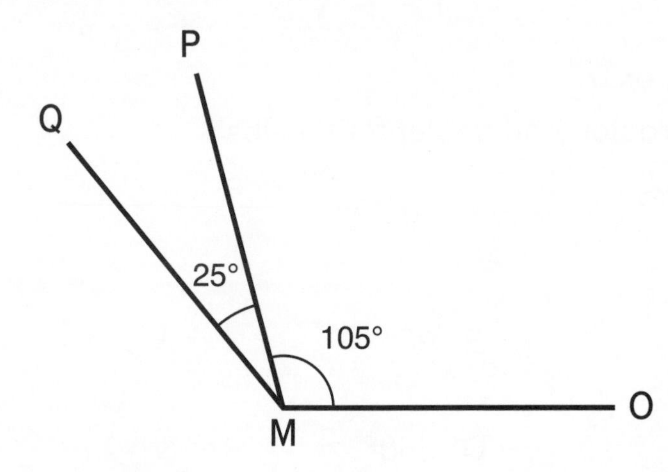

A ∠QMP **B** ∠PMO

C ∠QMO **D** ∠QPO

5 WXYZ is a rectangle. What is the measure of ∠ZXY?

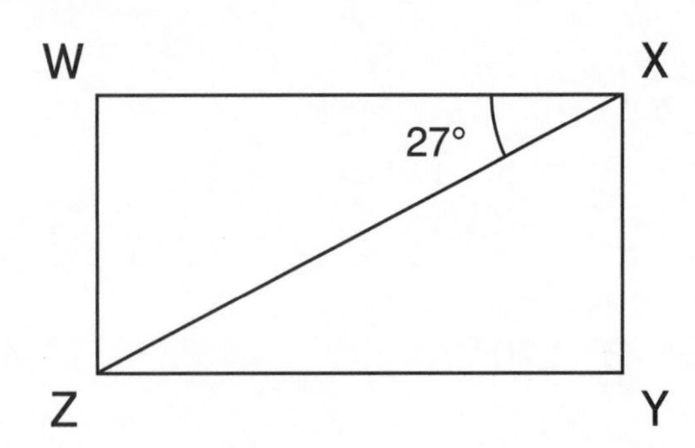

A 153° **B** 33°

C 117° **D** 63°

Section B (2 points each)

6 Find the measure of Angle a.

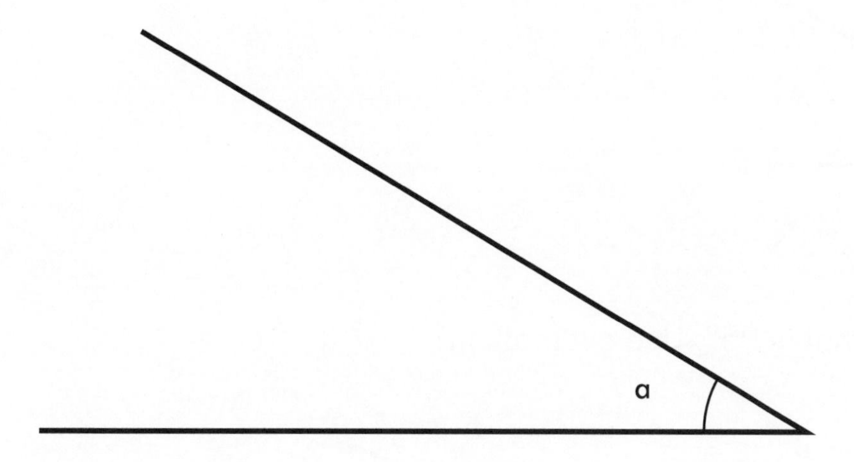

7 Find the measure of ∠XYZ.

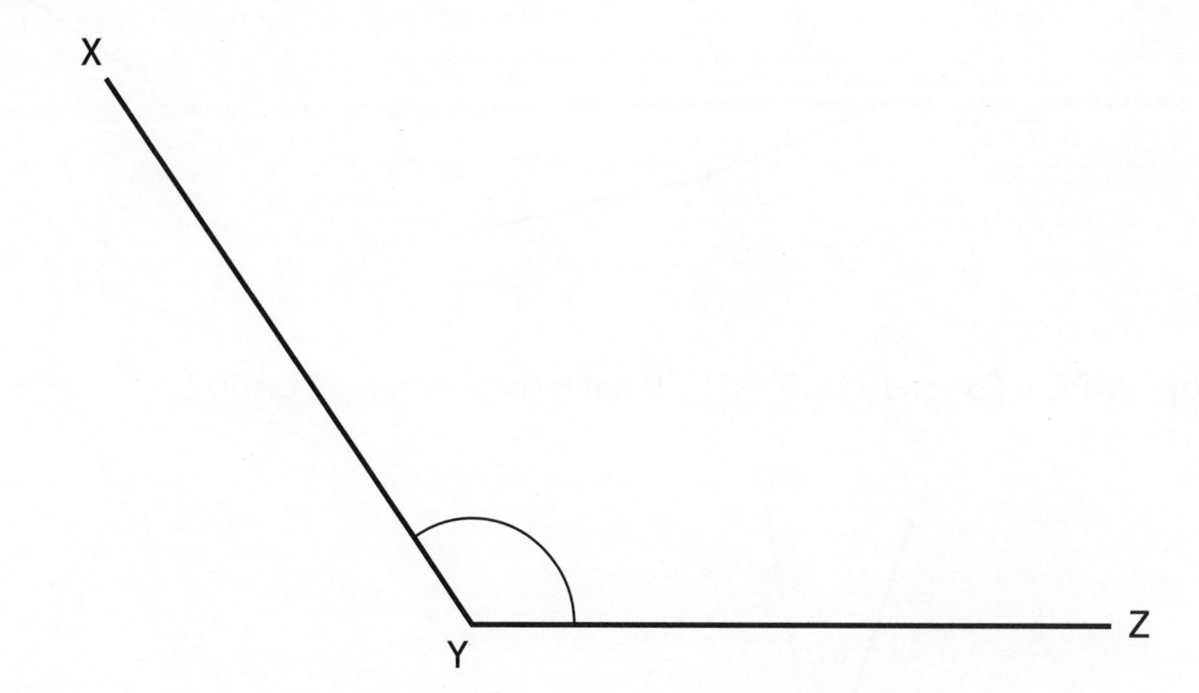

8. Name the marked angle using the given letters.

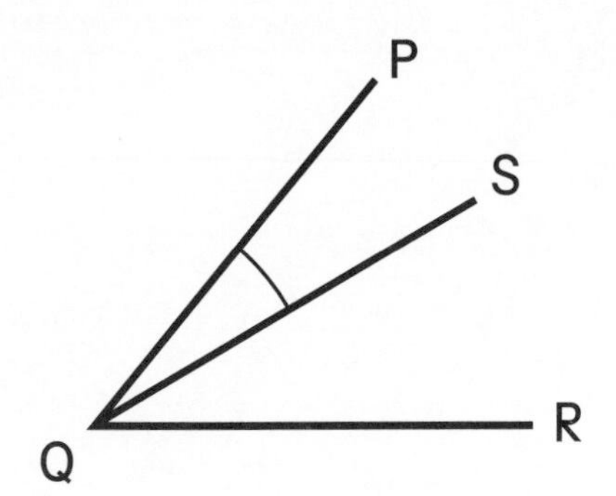

9. Circle the angle that is 95°. Use estimation.

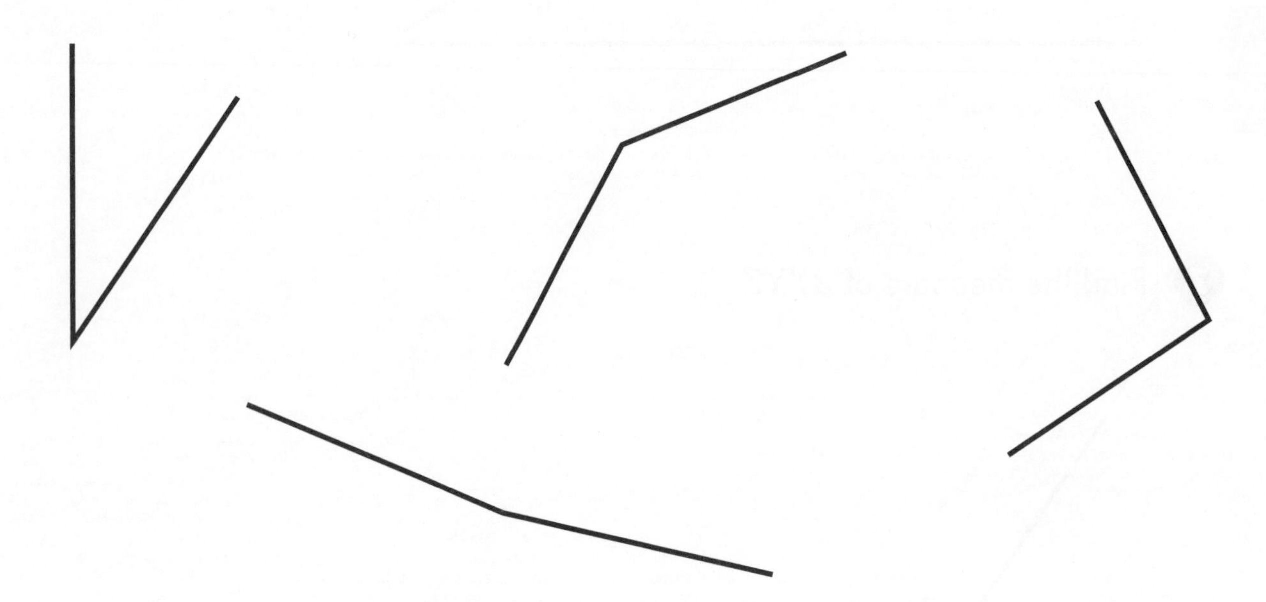

10. $\angle ABC = 55°$ and $\angle CBD = 31°$. What is the measure of $\angle ABD$?

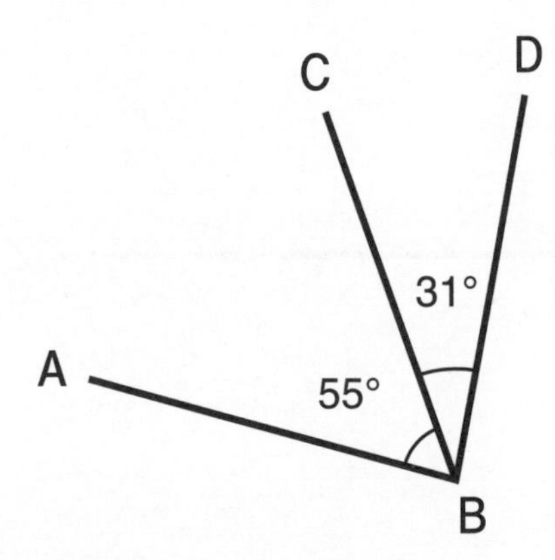

11 LM is a straight line. Find the measure of the unknown angle.

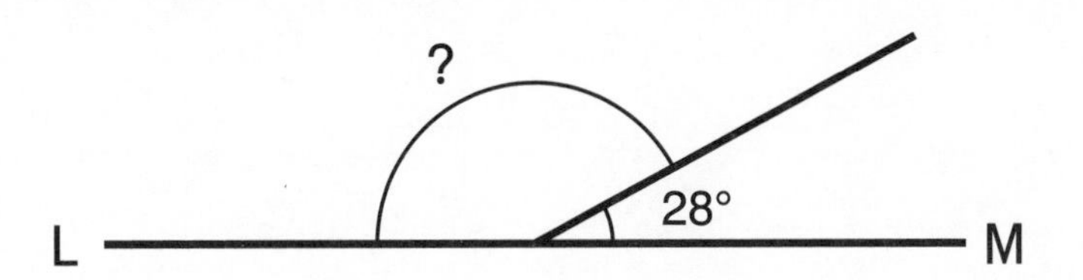

12 Find the measure of ∠a.

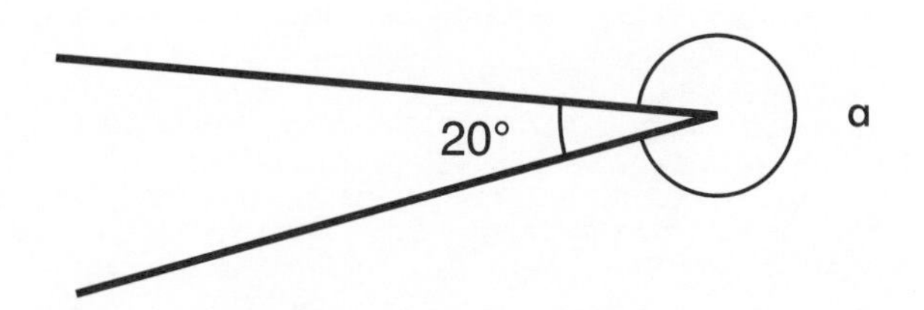

13 Mei is facing east. She turns 180° clockwise. What direction is she now facing?

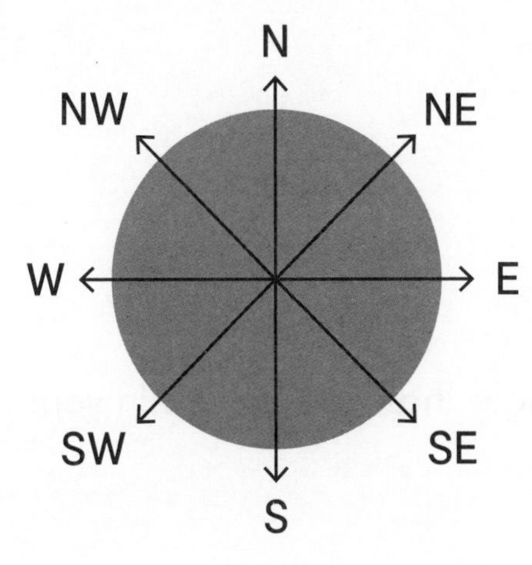

14. Draw a 35° angle.

15. (a) Draw a 110° angle.

(b) Calculate the measure of the reflex angle that was formed in your drawing for (a).

25 min Score

Name: ____________________

Date: ____________________

30

Test B

Chapter 15 Angles

Section A (2 points each)

Circle the correct option: **A**, **B**, **C**, or **D**.

You will need a set square, a protractor, and a ruler for this test.

1 $\frac{1}{2}$ turn = ____________

A $\frac{1}{2} \times 180°$

B $\frac{1}{2} \times 90°$

C $\frac{1}{2} \times 360°$

D $\frac{1}{2} \times 50°$

2 What is the size of Angle c?

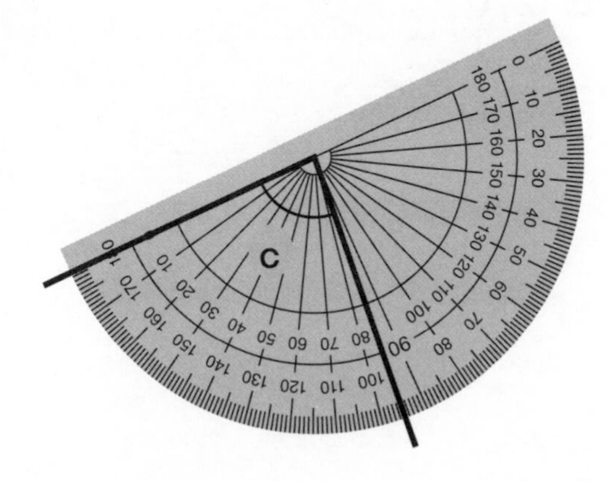

A 80°

B 85°

C 105°

D 95°

3 Which of the following is not a measure of an obtuse angle?

A 100°

B 93°

C 175°

D 75°

4 Dion is facing north. How many degrees does he have to turn counterclockwise to be facing east?

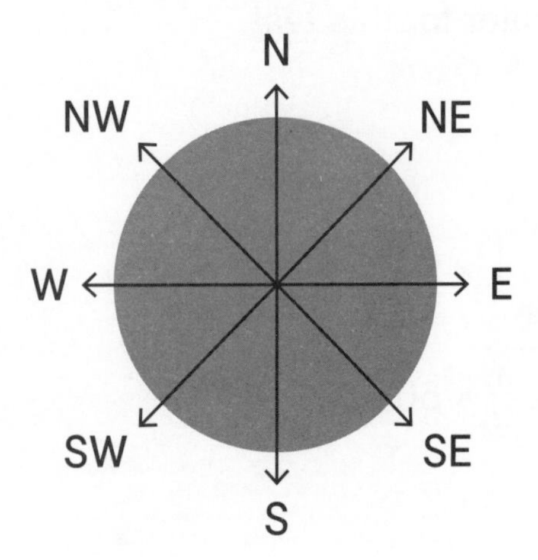

A 180°

B 270°

C 90°

D 360°

5 How many degrees are in $\frac{5}{12}$ of a turn?

A 150°

B 75°

C 120°

D 30°

Section B (2 points each)

6 Find the measure of ∠ABC.

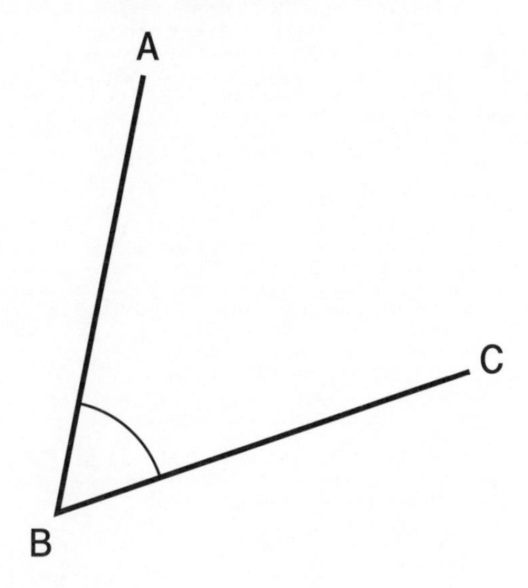

7 Find the measure of ∠m.

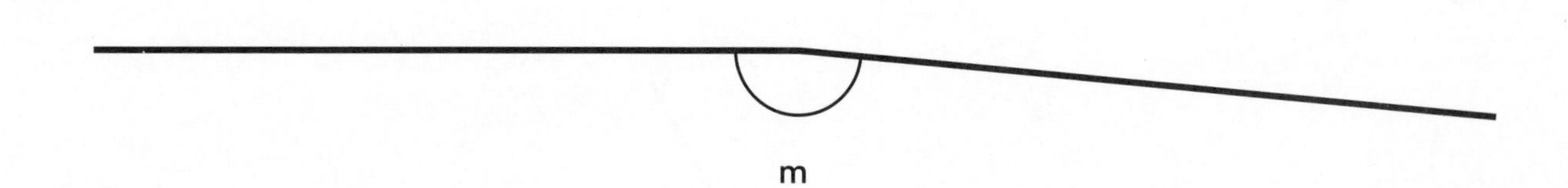

8 Name the marked angle using the given letters.

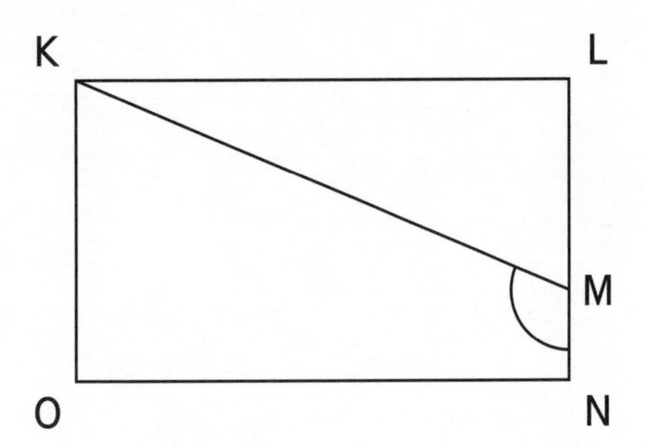

9 Find the measure of ∠a in the square.

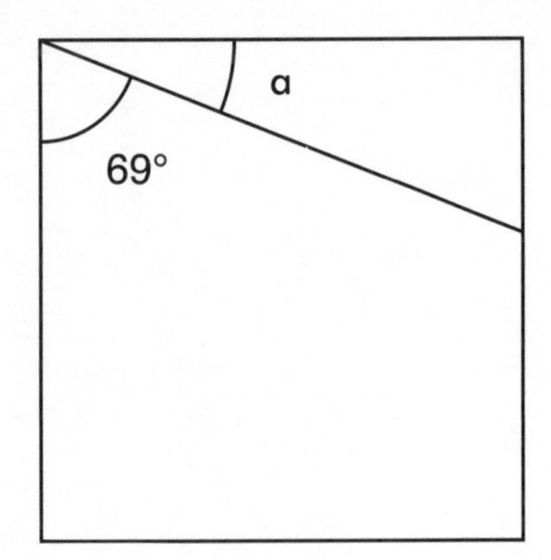

10 Find the measure of ∠VTU.

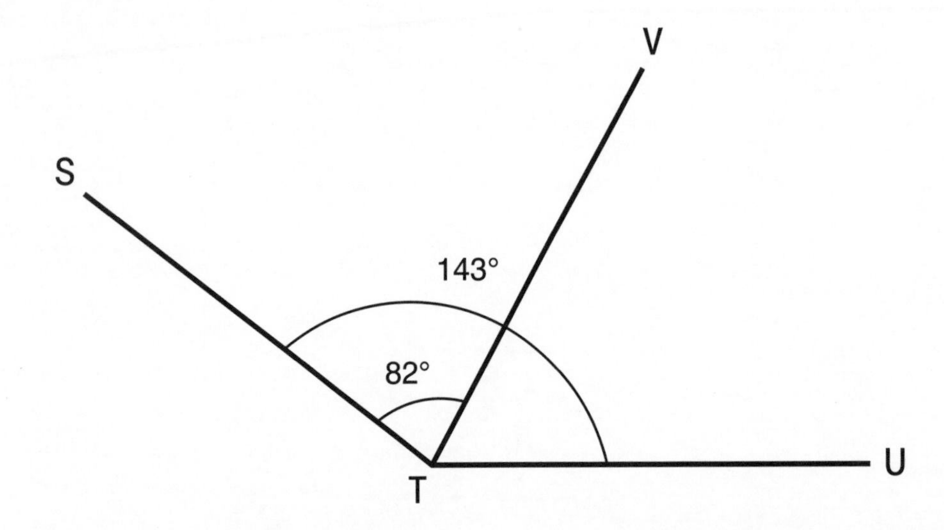

11. Draw a 145° angle.

12 DE is a straight line. Find the measure of the unknown angle.

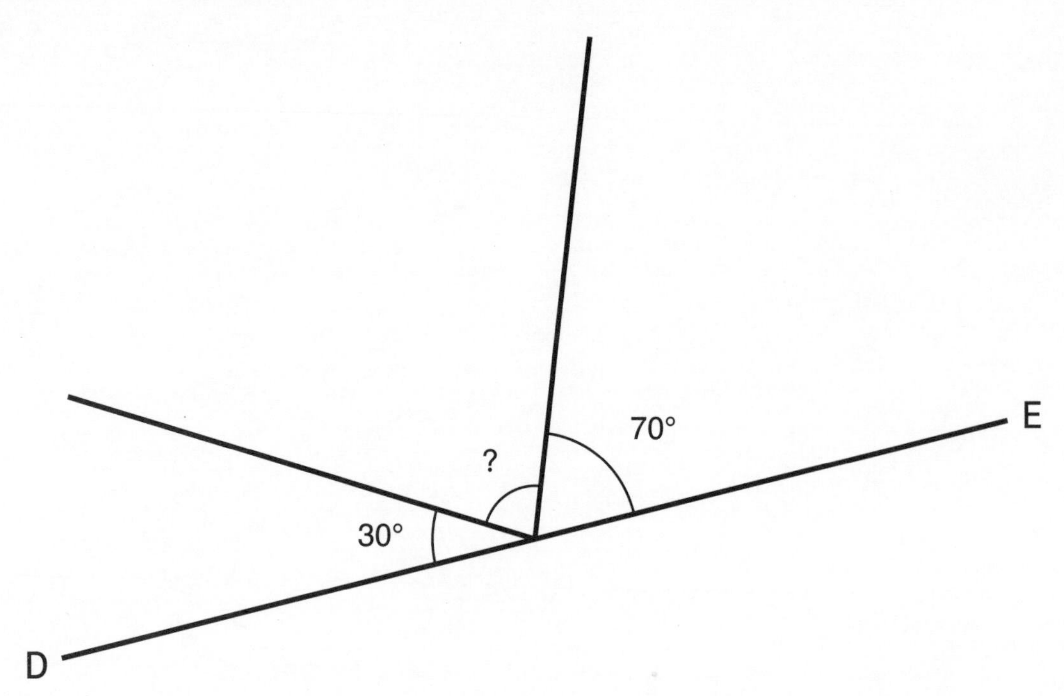

13 Check (✓) the statements that are true.

An acute angle is between 0° and 90°.	
A reflex angle is smaller than a straight angle.	
An obtuse angle is less than 90°.	
A full turn is equal to 360°.	

14 What is the measure of ∠m?

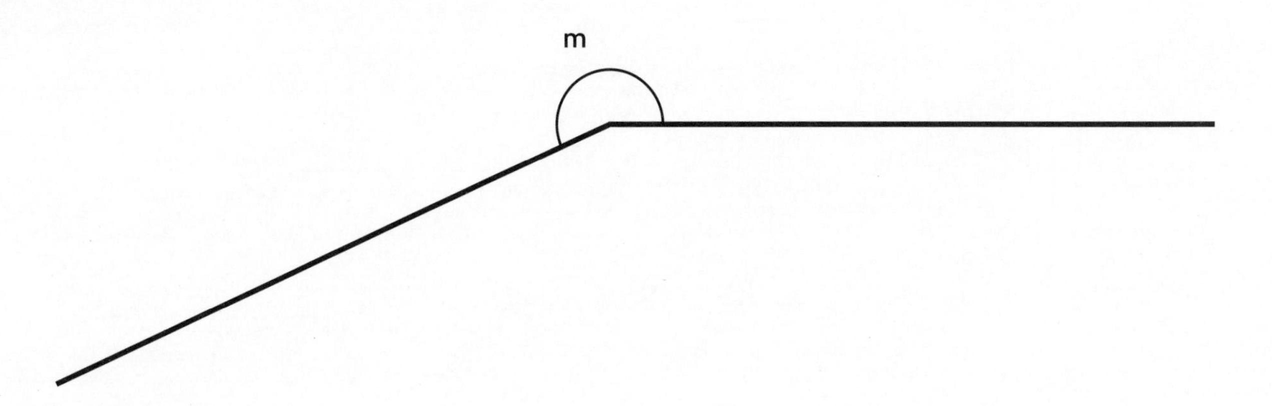

15 (a) Draw a 75° angle.

(b) Calculate the measure of the reflex angle that was formed in your drawing for (a).

25 min Score

Name: ______________________

Date: ______________________

Score
30

Test A

Chapter 16 Lines and Shapes

Section A (2 points each)

Circle the correct option: **A**, **B**, **C**, or **D**.

You will need a set square and a ruler for this test.

1 Which sides are perpendicular to each other in this triangle?

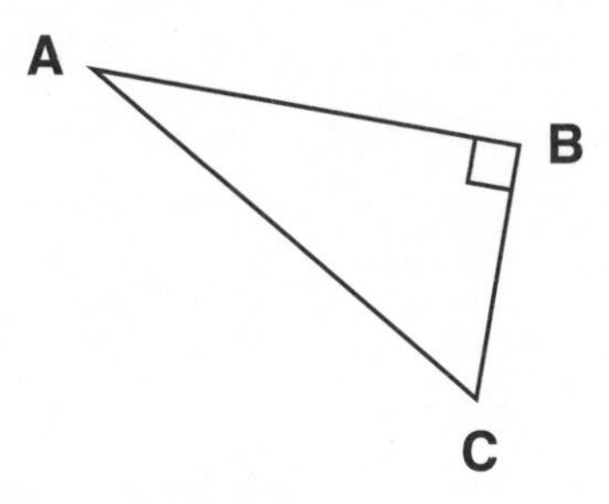

A AB ⊥ AC **B** BC ⊥ AC

C CB ⊥ CA **D** AB ⊥ BC

2 Which lines are perpendicular to QR in this rectangle?

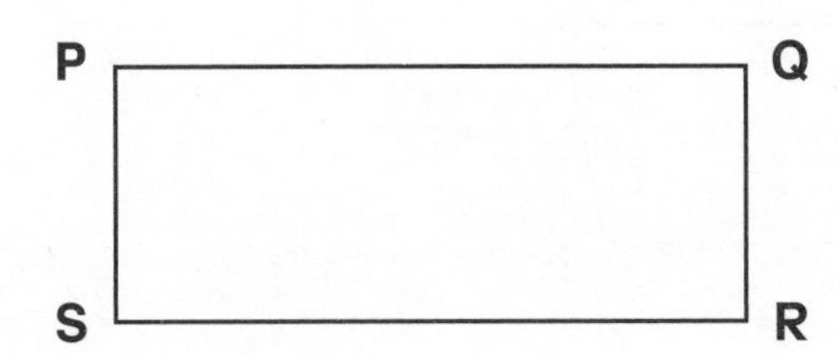

A PS and SR **B** RS and PS

C PQ and SR **D** PS and PQ

3 How many pairs of parallel lines are there in the figure?

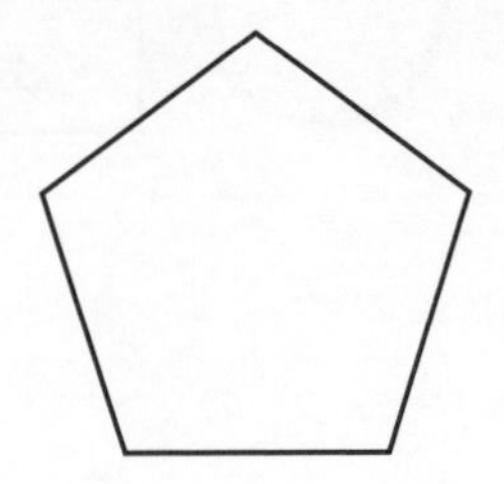

A 0 **B** 1

C 2 **D** 3

4 On which figure is the dotted line a line of symmetry?

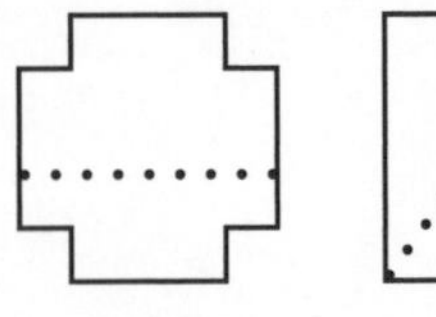

E F G H

A E **B** F

C G **D** H

5 Which figure has more than one line of symmetry?

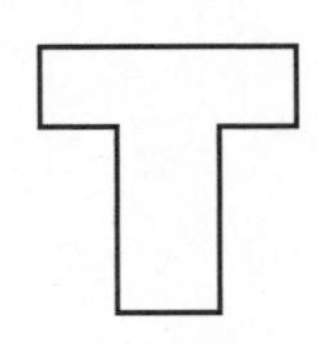

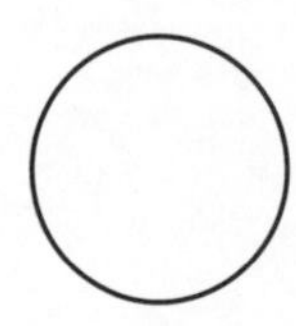

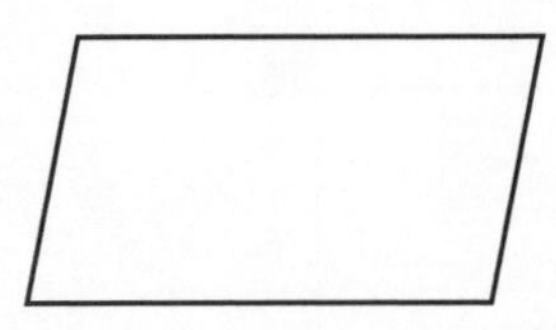

M N O P

A M **B** O

C N **D** P

Section B (2 points each)

6 Name each pair of perpendicular sides in the figure. Use a set square to identify right angles.

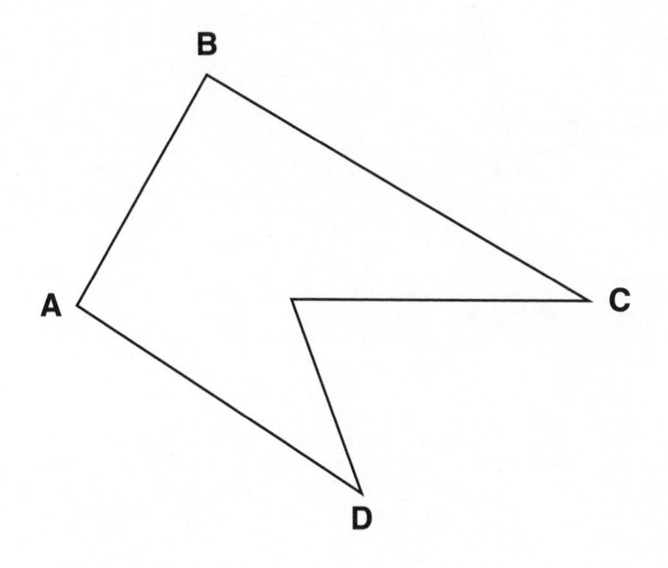

7 Which of the following figures are parallelograms?

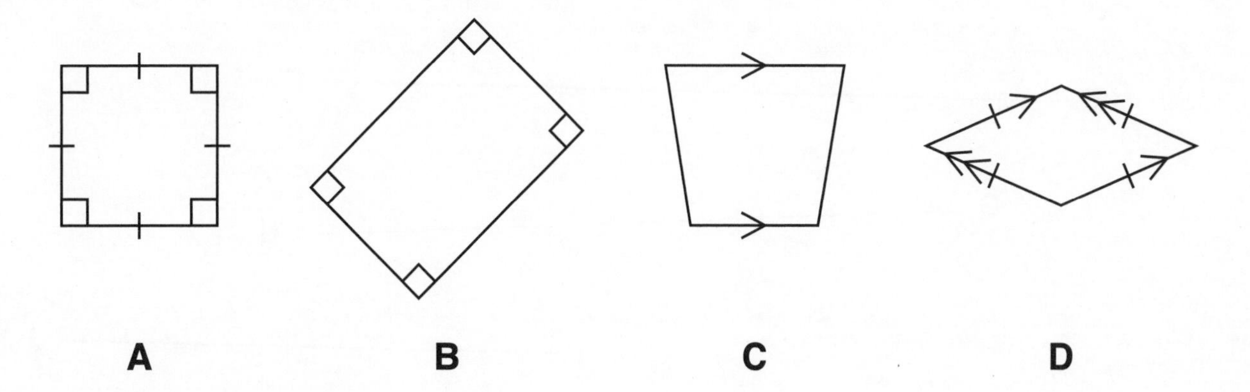

8 Name pairs of parallel lines in the following figure. Use a set square to identify right angles.

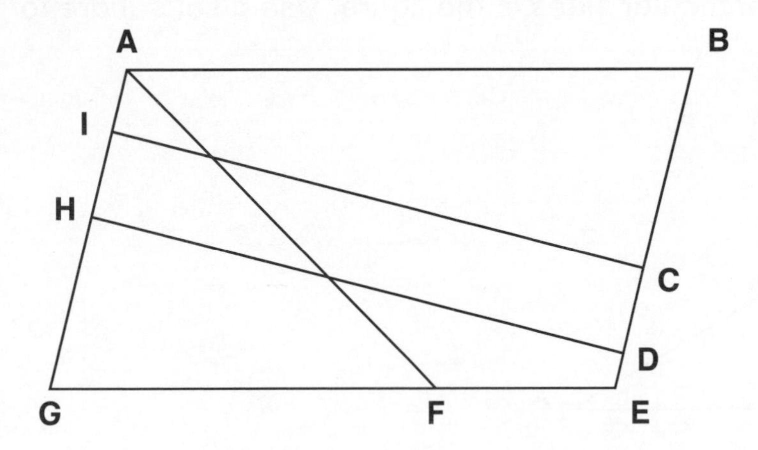

9 Use a ruler and a set square to identify lines parallel to AB. Name them.

A B

C D

E F

G H

I J

10 Use a ruler and a set square to draw a line perpendicular to AB that passes through Point C.

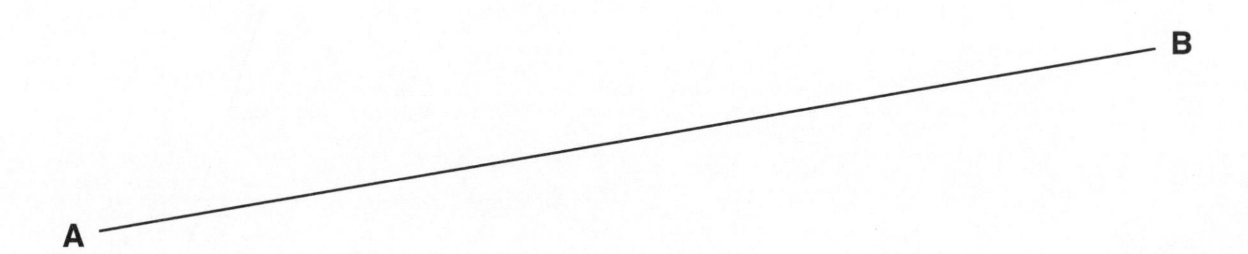

11 Use a ruler and a set square to draw a line through Point Z parallel to Line XY.

X

Z

Y

12 Name the pairs of lines that are parallel to each other.

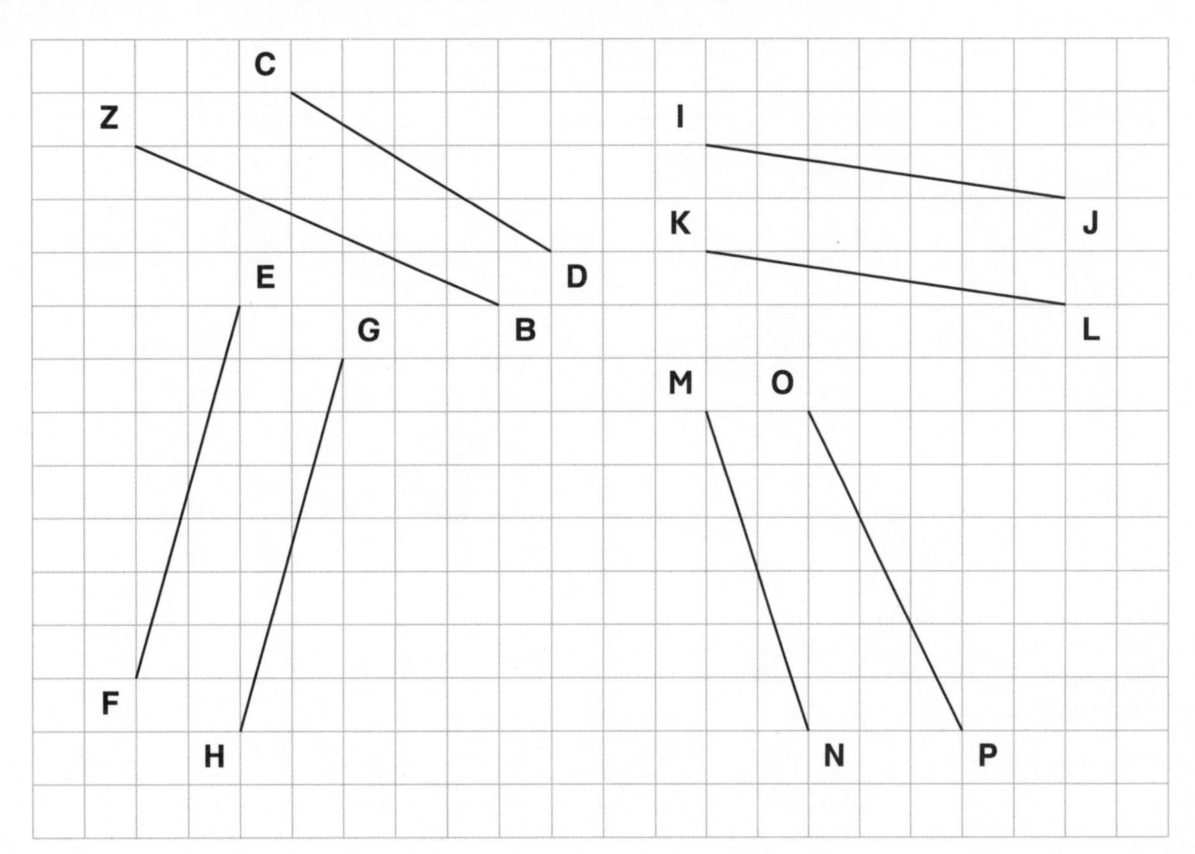

13 Draw a line of symmetry for the following figure.

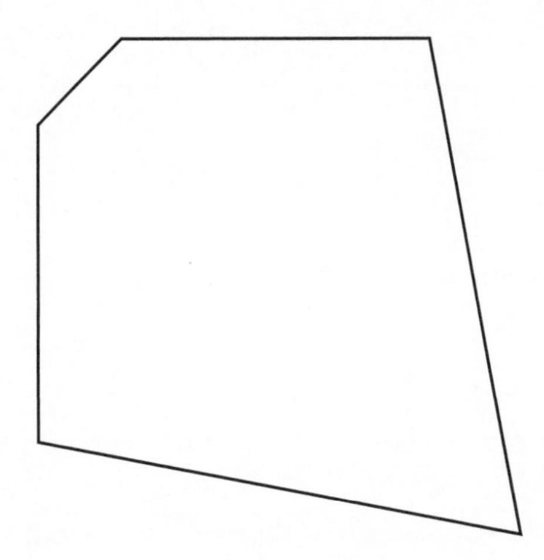

14 Complete the figure so that the dotted line is a line of symmetry.

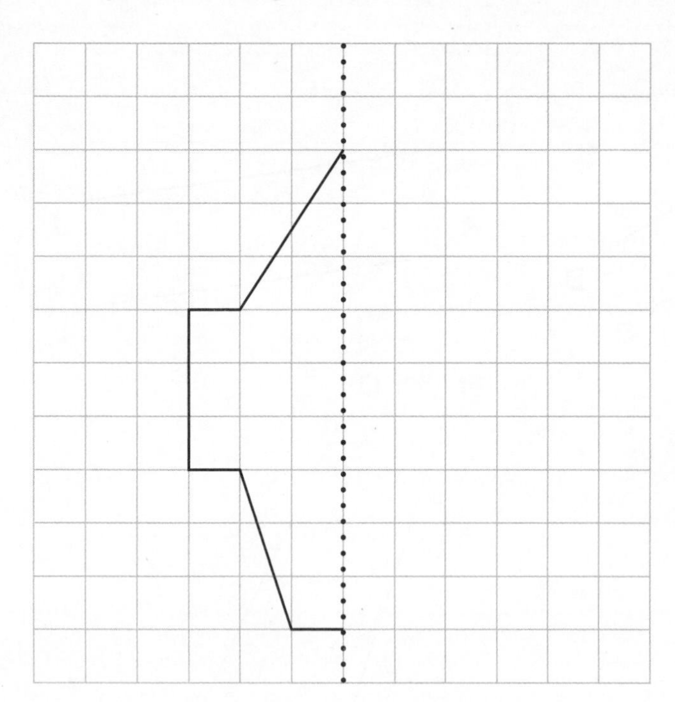

15 Shade two more squares on the grid to make this figure symmetrical.

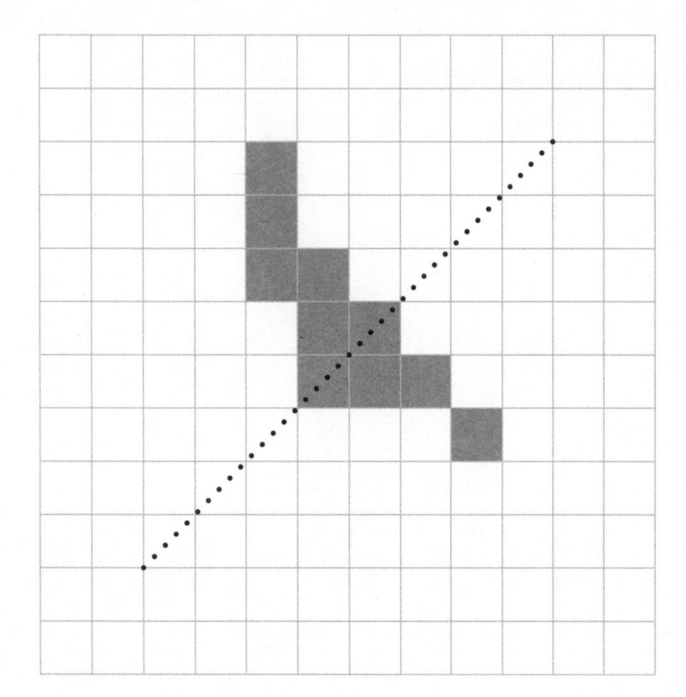

25 min Score

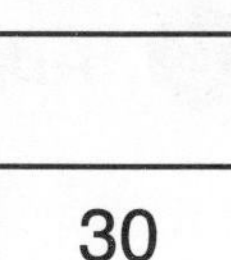

Name: ______________________________

Date: ______________________________

30

Test B

Chapter 16 Lines and Shapes

Section A (2 points each)

Circle the correct option: **A**, **B**, **C**, or **D**.

You will need a set square and a ruler for this test.

1 Which lines are perpendicular to line MN?

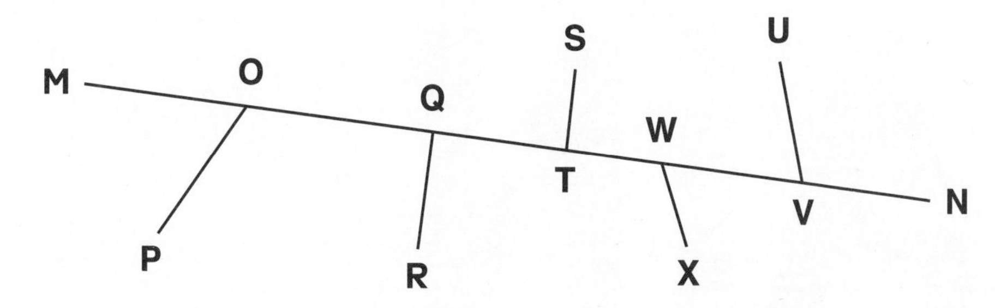

A WX and UV

B ST and QR

C OP and ST

D QR and WX

2 Which pairs of lines are not perpendicular to each other in this rectangle?

E F

H G

A EF and FG

B HG and EH

C EF and HG

D FH and HG

3 AB is parallel to CD. Which line has the same length as GH?

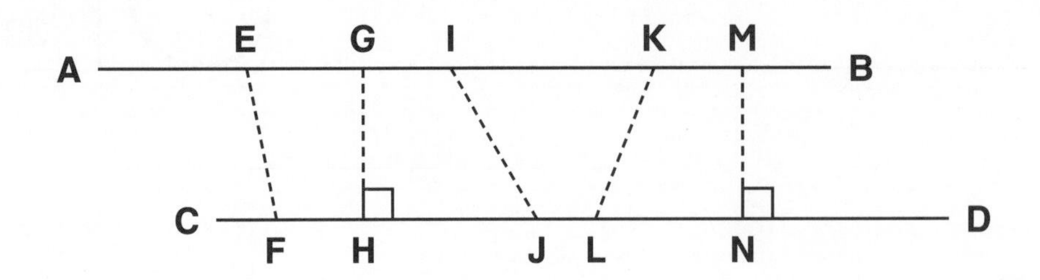

A MN

B KL

C EF

D IJ

4 Which two letters in this word have at least one line of symmetry?

RAIN

A R and A

B I and N

C A and I

D R and N

5 How many lines of symmetry does this figure have?

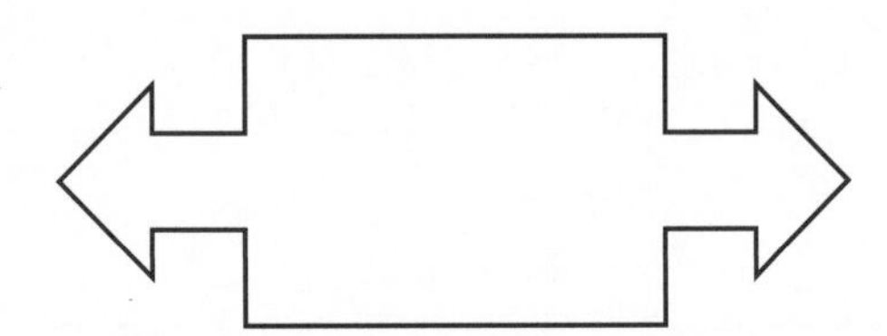

A 1

B 4

C 3

D 2

Section B (2 points each)

6 Name each pair of perpendicular sides in the polygon.
Use a set square to identify right angles.

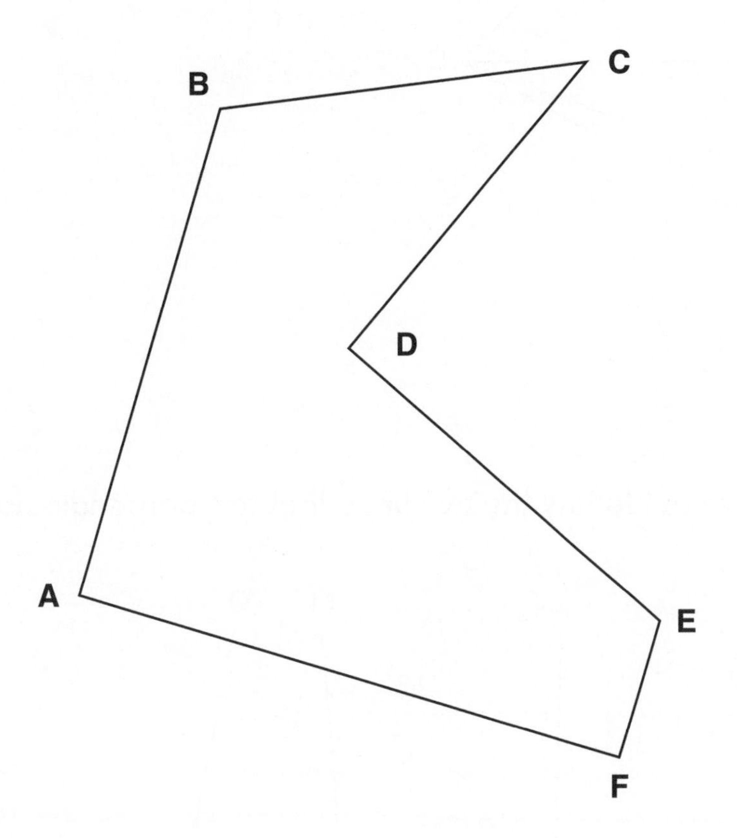

7 Put an X next to the statement that is NOT true.

Opposite sides of a parallelogram are equal in length.	
Some parallelograms have four right angles.	
All trapezoids are parallelograms.	
A parallelogram has two pairs of parallel sides.	

8 Name pairs of parallel lines in the following figure.

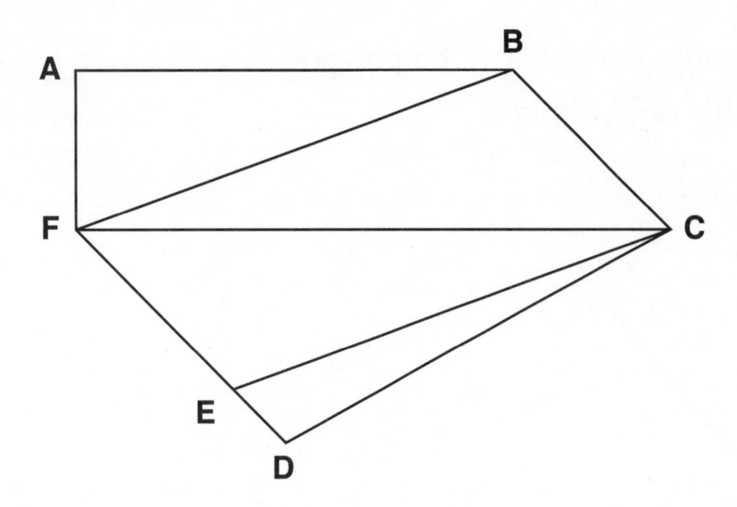

9 Use a ruler and set square to identify the two lines that are perpendicular to GH.

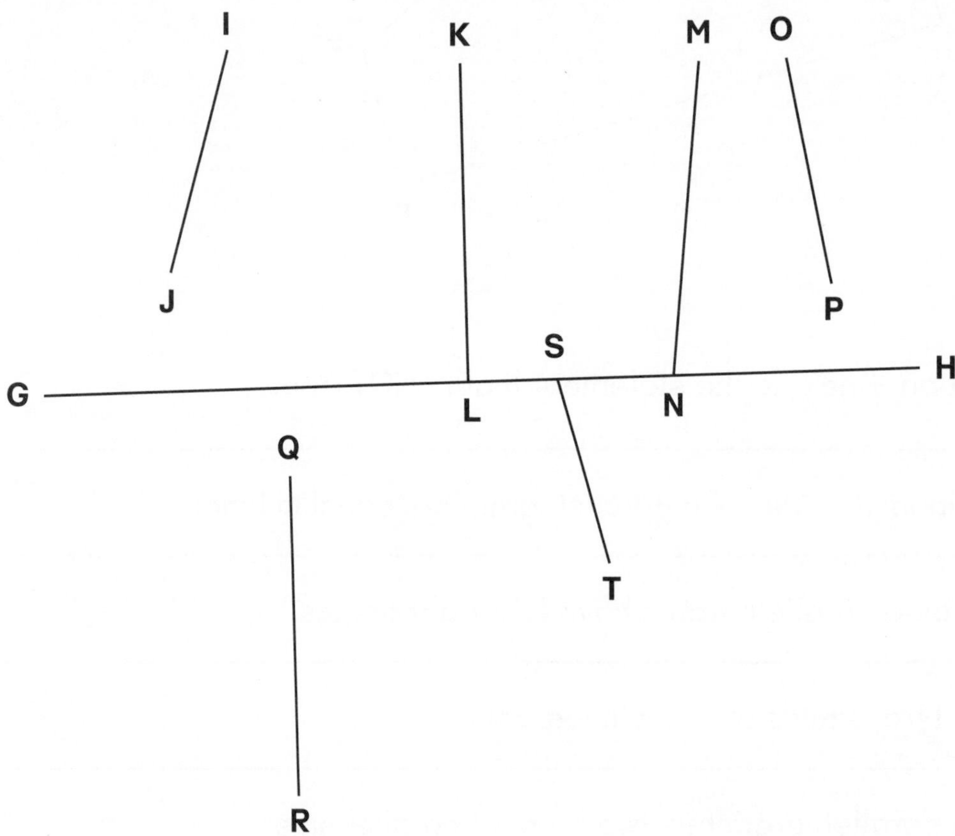

10 Use a ruler and a set square to draw one line perpendicular and one line parallel to AB through the given point.

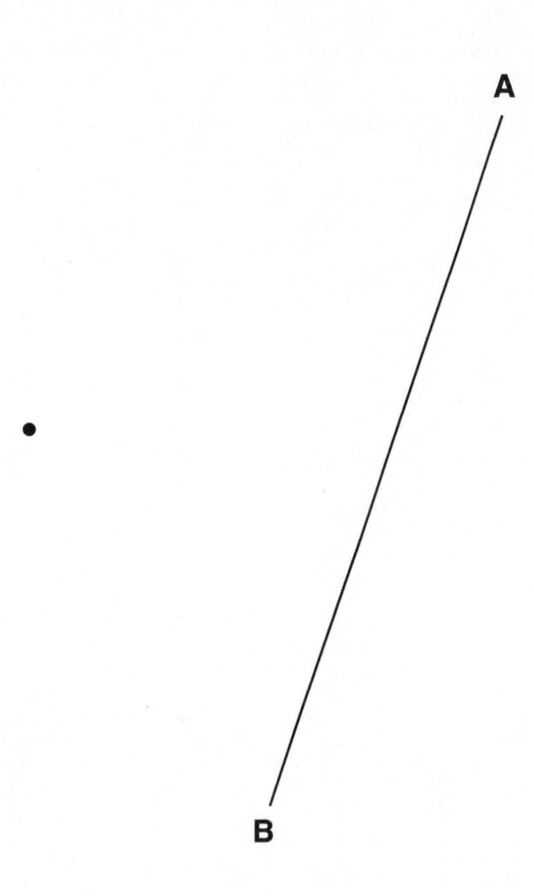

11 Use a ruler and a set square to draw a line parallel to and 3 cm away from EF.

E

F

12 Check (✓) the statements that are true.

A rhombus has two pairs of parallel sides.	
A rectangle has more than 2 pairs of perpendicular sides.	
All quadrilaterals have at least one pair of parallel sides.	
All parallelograms have at least one pair of perpendicular sides.	

13 Draw a line of symmetry for the following figure.

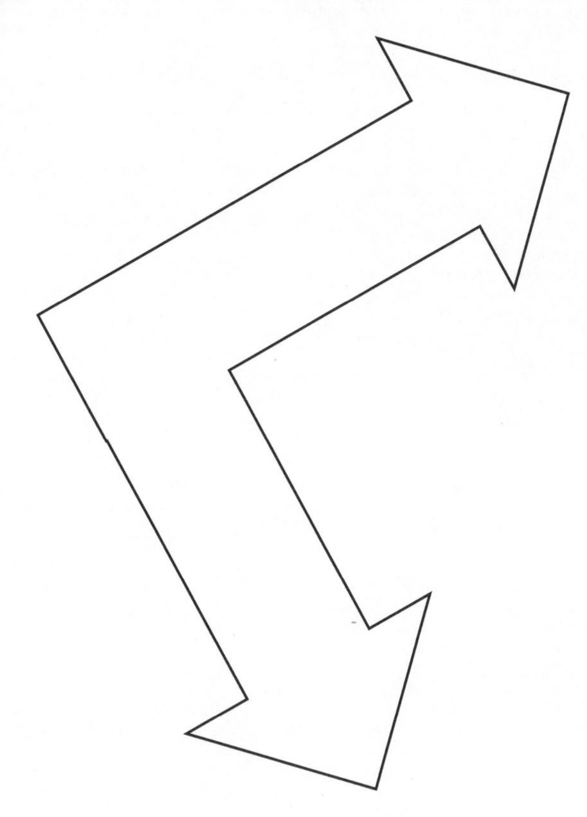

14 Complete the figure so that the dotted line is a line of symmetry.

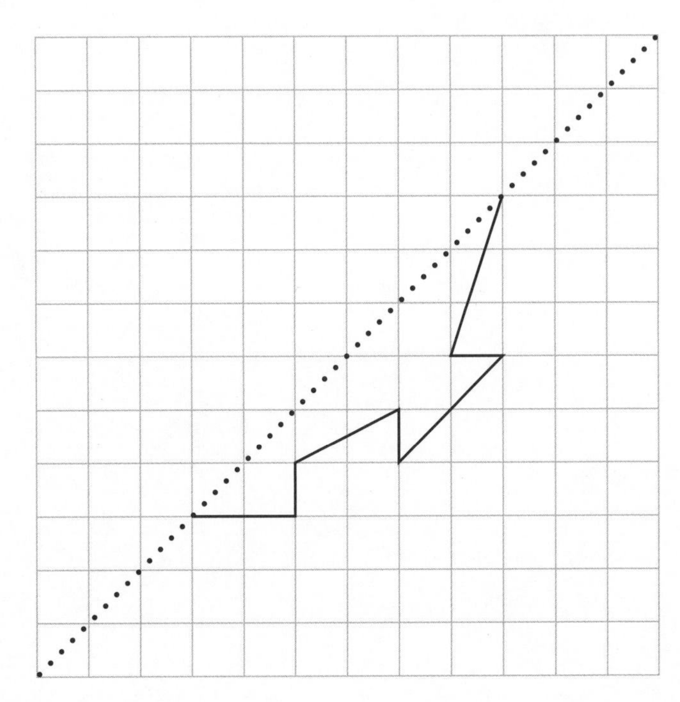

15 Complete the symmetrical figure by shading 3 more squares on the grid.

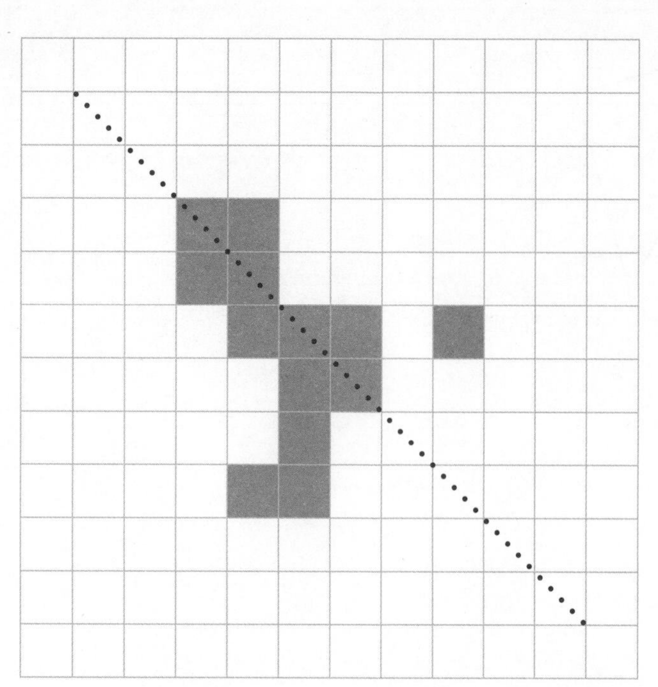

25 min Score

Name: ______________________

Date: ______________________

30

Test A

Chapter 17 Properties of Cuboids

Section A (2 points each)

Circle the correct option: **A**, **B**, **C**, or **D**.

1 Which of the following edges has the same length as Edge AB?

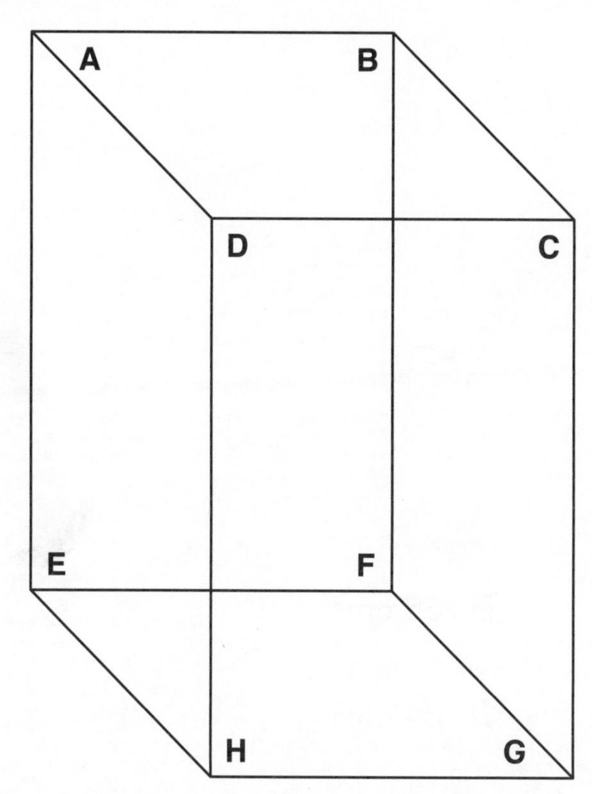

A AE

B BC

C HG

D GC

2 How many faces of a cube are the same size and shape?

A 4

B 0

C 2

D 6

3 What is the area of Face JIMN?

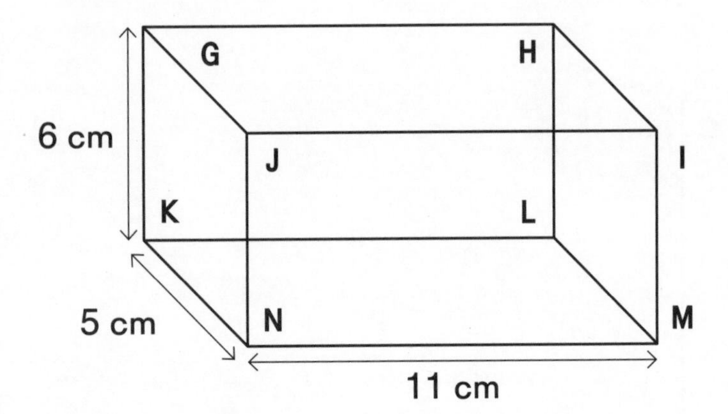

A 30 cm^2

B 66 cm^2

C 55 cm^2

D 34 cm^2

4 Face ABCD and Face _______ are parallel to each other.

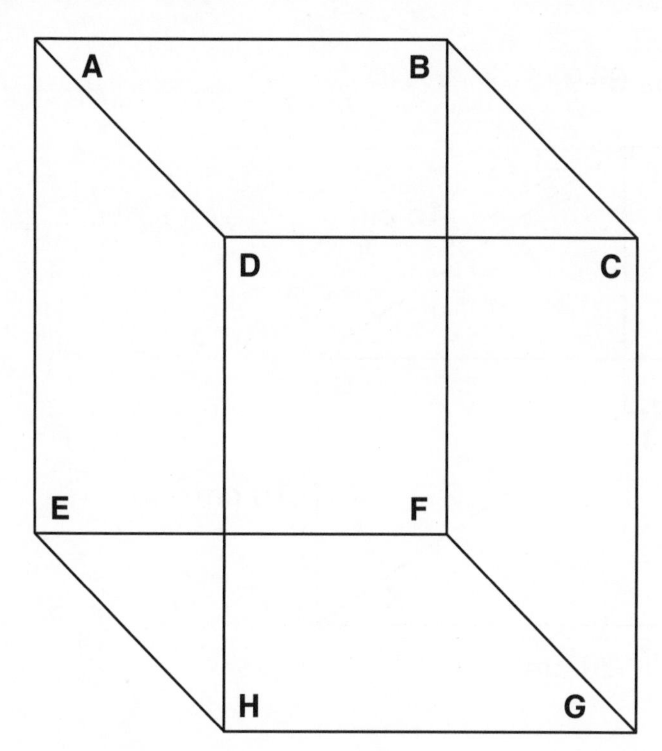

A ABFE

B EFGH

C BCGF

D ADHE

5 Which of the following is not a net of a cube?

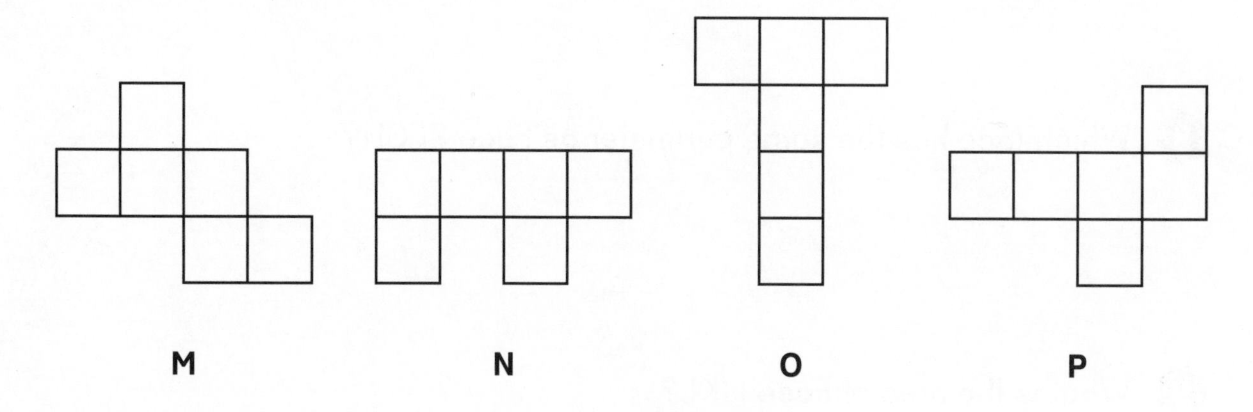

A O

B M

C N

D P

Section B (2 points each)

Use this cuboid to answer questions 6–9.

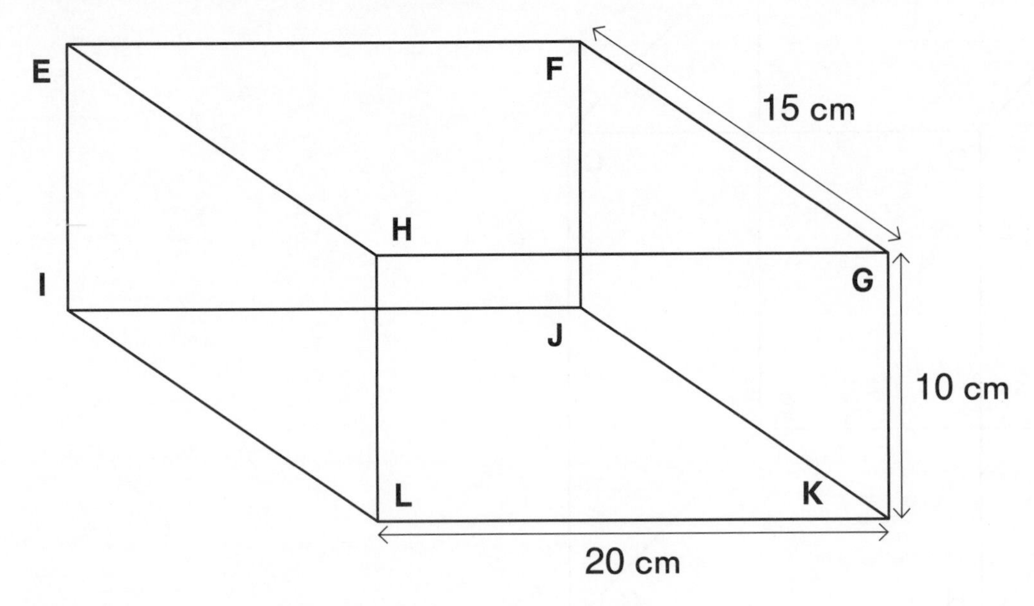

6. List all the edges that are 10 cm long.

7. Which face has the same shape and size as Face FGKJ?

8. Which face has the same perimeter as Face EFGH?

9. What is the area of Face IJKL?

Use this cuboid to answer questions 10–13.

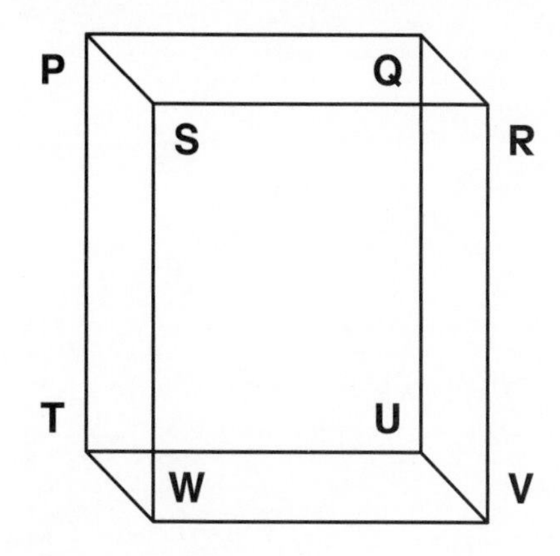

10. Name two edges that are parallel to Edge PS.

11. Which face is parallel to Face PQUT?

12. Face QRVU and Face TUVW are perpendicular to each other at Edge ______.

13. Faces PQUT, SRVW, QRVU, and ______ are perpendicular to Face PQRS.

Use this net of a cuboid to answers questions 14–15.

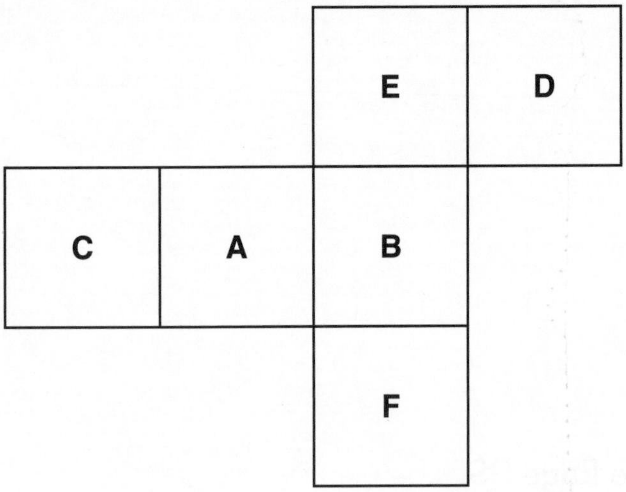

		E	D
C	A	B	
		F	

When the net is folded:

14 Which face will be parallel to Face E?

15 Face B will be perpendicular to Face A, Face E, Face _______, and Face _______.

25 min Score

Name: ______________________

Date: ______________________

30

Test B

Chapter 17 Properties of Cuboids

Section A (2 points each)

Circle the correct option: **A**, **B**, **C**, or **D**.

1 A cuboid has _______ vertices.

A 8 **B** 4

C 2 **D** 6

2 How many edges of a cube are the same length?

A 8 **B** 4

C 12 **D** 6

3 What is the area of Face HIML?

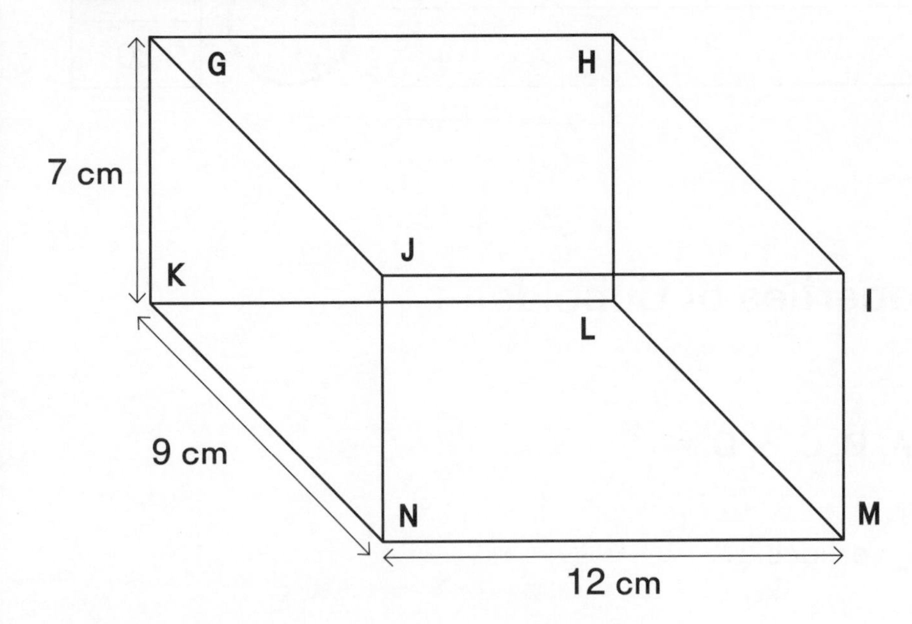

A 108 cm^2

B 84 cm^2

C 32 cm^2

D 63 cm^2

4 How many faces are perpendicular to Face QRST?

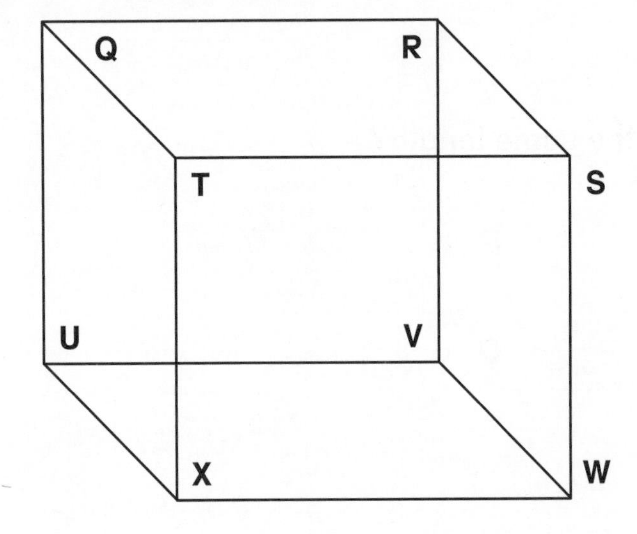

A 8

B 3

C 4

D 2

5 This is the net of a cube. When the net is folded, which face will be opposite E?

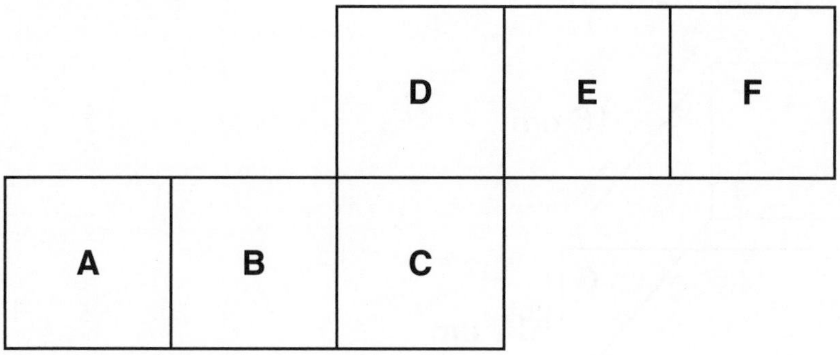

		D	E	F
A	B	C		

A D

B B

C F

D C

Section B (2 points each)

Use this cuboid to answer questions 6–9.

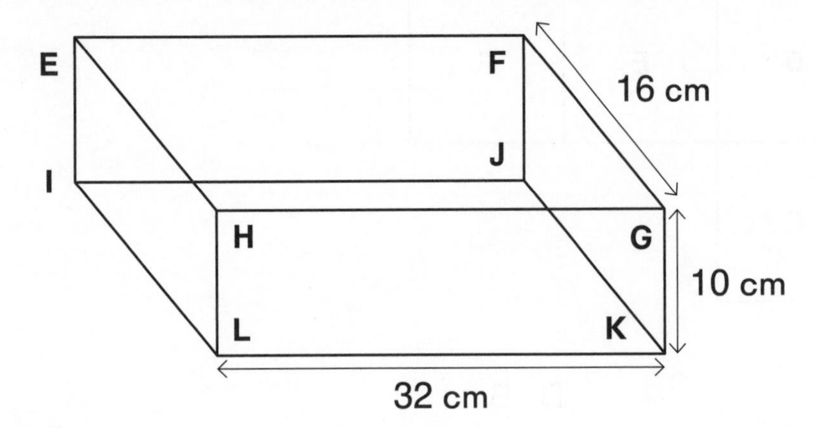

6. Name four edges that do NOT have the same length as Edge IL.

7. What is the total length of Edge IJ and Edge EH?

8. What is the perimeter of Face EFJI?

9. List the faces that have an area of 160 cm^2.

Use this cuboid to answer questions 10–13.

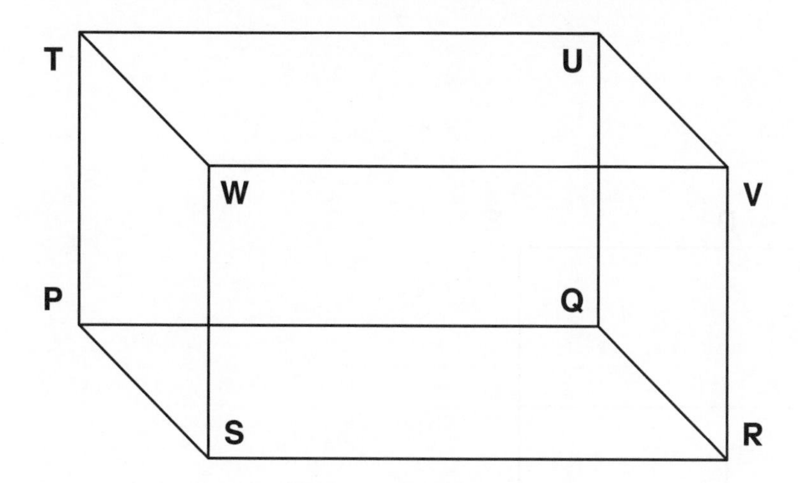

10 Name three faces that Face UVRQ is NOT parallel to.

11 Faces _______ and _______ meet at Edge TP.

12 Which two faces are perpendicular to both Face WVRS and Face PQRS?

13 Face TUVW and Face _______ are not perpendicular to each other.

Use this net of a cuboid to answer questions 14–15.

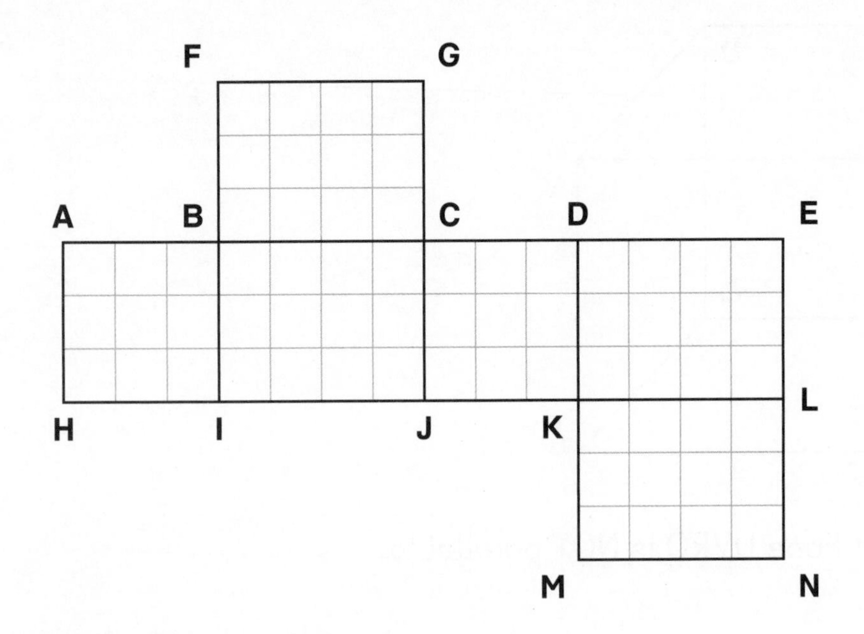

When the net is folded:

14 Which edge will touch Edge DE?

15 Face FGCB and Face _______ will be perpendicular to both Faces CDKJ and BCJI.

60 min Score

Name: ______________________

Date: ______________________

80

Test A

Year-end Assessment

Section A (2 points each)

Circle the correct option: **A**, **B**, **C**, or **D**.

You will need a set square, a protractor, and a ruler for this test.

1 What is the sum of the first four factors of 36?

A 15 **B** 10

C 11 **D** 4

2 Which of the following is a common multiple of 2, 3, and 4?

A 6 **B** 8

C 12 **D** 16

3 3,950 = ☐ hundreds + 5 tens

A 9 **B** 39

C 3 **D** 395

4. What is the value of 9 in 314.95?

A 9

B 0.09

C 90

D 0.9

5. What does the digit 8 stand for in 53.78?

A 8 tenths

B 8 ones

C 8 hundredths

D 8 hundreds

6. 27 qt = ______________

A 6 gal 3 qt

B 6 gal 1 qt

C 2 gal 7 qt

D 5 gal 3 qt

7. What is 4.25 expressed as a mixed number in simplest form?

A $4\frac{2}{5}$

B $4\frac{25}{100}$

C $4\frac{1}{4}$

D $\frac{42}{5}$

8 $50.08 \times 6 =$ ☐

A 301.08

B 300.48

C 300.08

D 301.48

9 What is $\frac{1}{4}$ minutes in seconds?

A 6

B 15

C 20

D 60

10 A square mirror has an area of 49 in^2. What is its perimeter in feet and inches?

A 2 ft 8 in

B 2 ft 4 in

C 2 ft

D 1 ft 2 in

11 5.45 rounded to 1 decimal place is ________.

A 5.5

B 6

C 5

D 5.4

12 $0.35 \div 7 =$ ☐

A 5

B 0.5

C 0.05

D 3.5

13 What is the measure of ∠SQR?

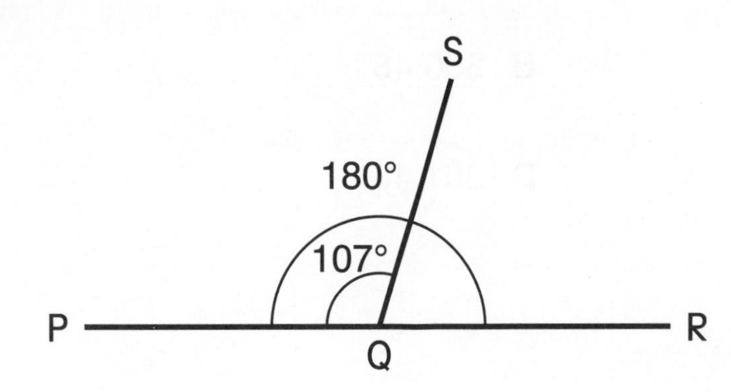

A 80° **B** 17°

C 107° **D** 73°

14 What fraction of a full turn is shown in the diagram below?

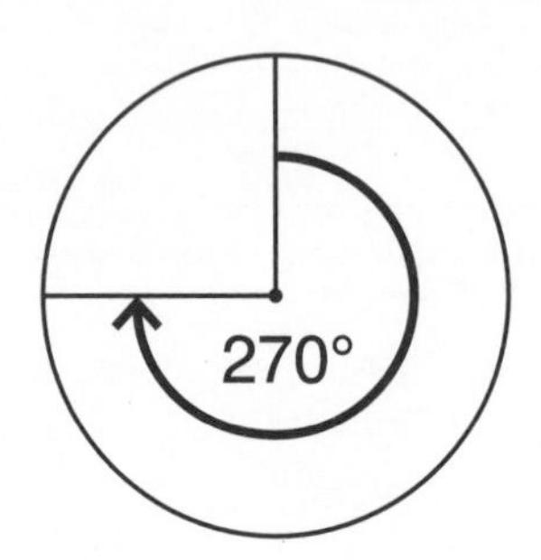

A $\frac{1}{4}$ **B** $\frac{1}{2}$

C $\frac{27}{100}$ **D** $\frac{3}{4}$

15 How many pairs of parallel lines does a parallelogram have?

A 0 **B** 2

C 4 **D** 1

Section B (2 points each)

16 Round 51,741 to the nearest ten thousand.

17 Write 9 ones 2 hundredths as a decimal.

18 Write 52.15 in expanded form.

19 A baby shark is $5\frac{3}{4}$ ft long. How long is the shark in inches?

The line graph shows the number of pies sold by a bakery last week.
Use the graph to answer questions 20–22.

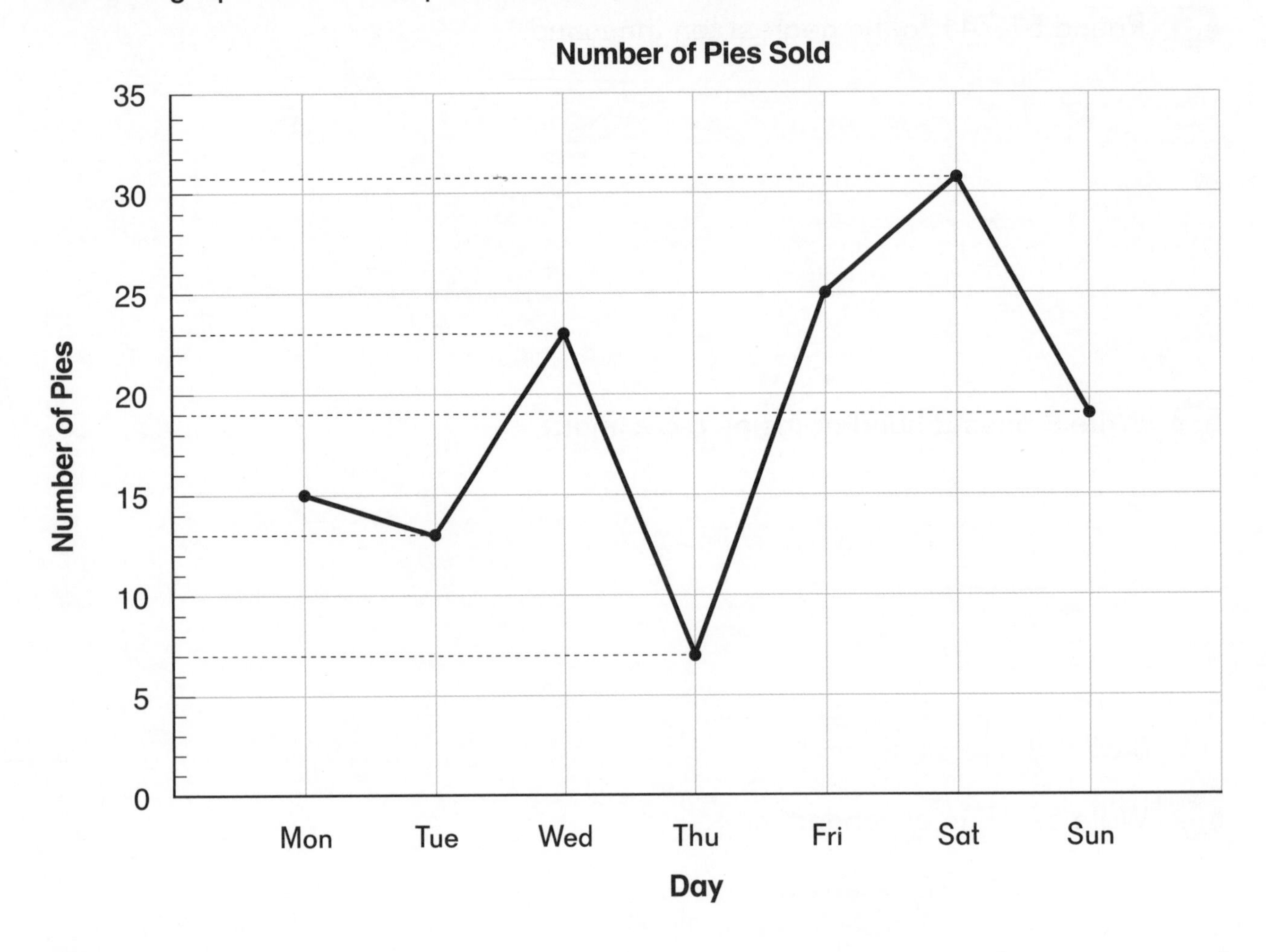

20 Between which two days was there the sharpest decrease in the sales of pies?

21 The bakery sold the pies at \$16.50 each. How much did the bakery receive from selling pies on Thursday?

22 Express the number of pies sold on Friday as a fraction of the total number of pies sold on Friday, Saturday, and Sunday. Express the answer in simplest form.

23 Arrange the numbers from least to greatest.

$0.72, \frac{7}{20}, 7.2, \frac{2}{10}$

______ ______ ______ ______

24 Complete the equation.

$8.36 = 8 + \frac{\square}{10} + \frac{6}{\square}$

25 A square has a perimeter of 7.2 cm. What is the length of its side?

Name two pairs of perpendicular lines in the diagram below.

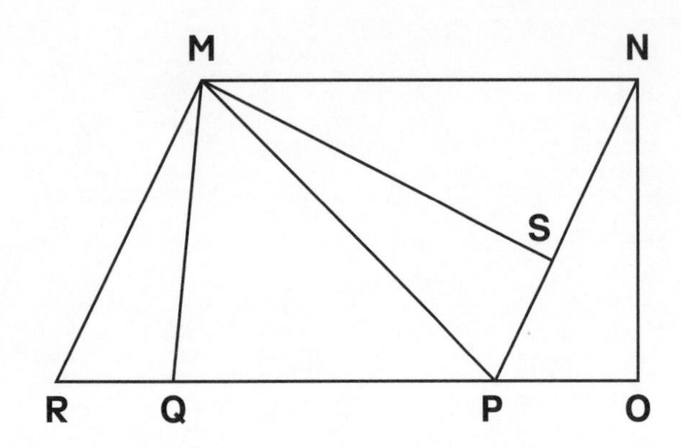

Find the measure of Angle e.

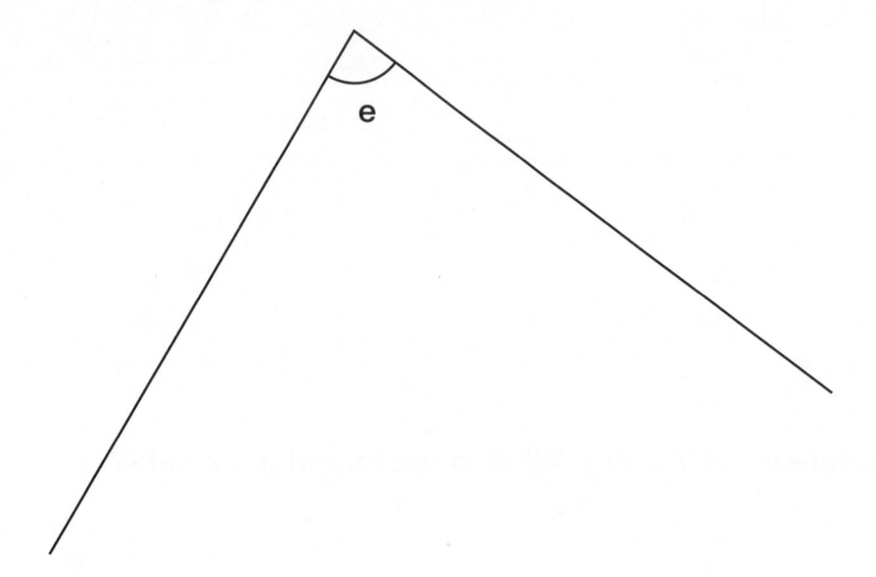

28 Cross out the figures that do not have a line of symmetry.

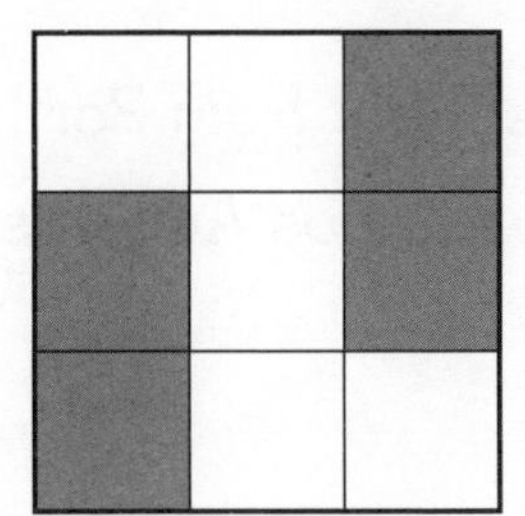

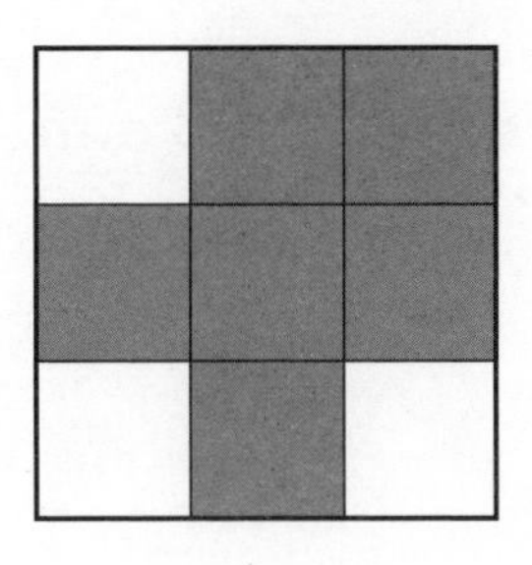

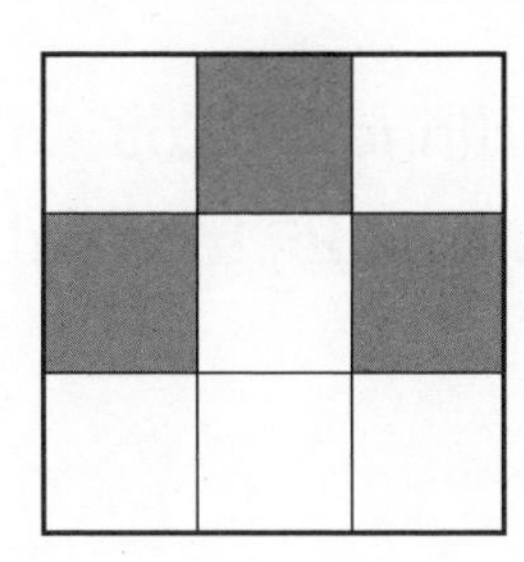

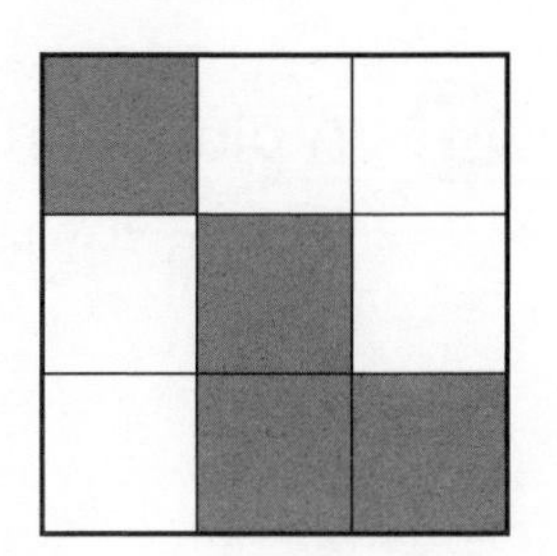

Use this cuboid to answer questions 29–30.

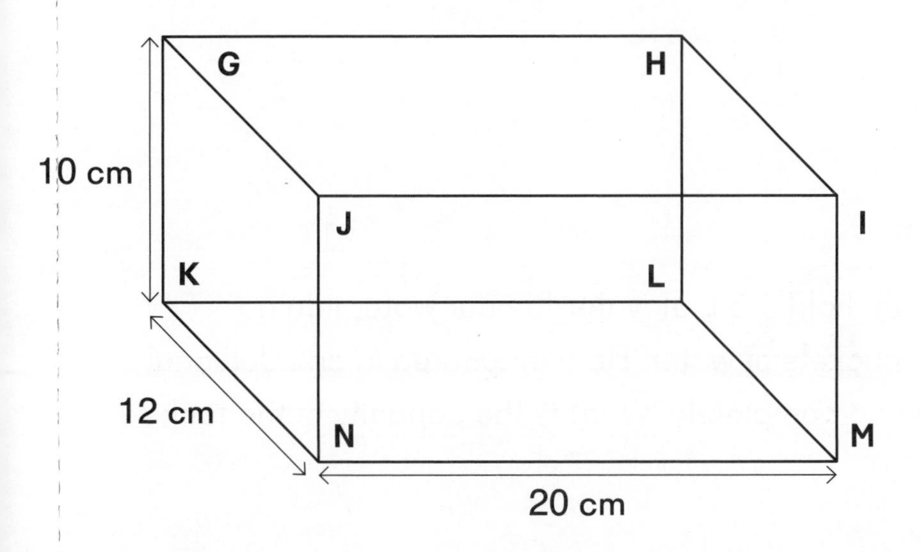

29 What is the area of Face GHLK?

30 Name two edges that are parallel to Edge LM.

Section C (4 points each)

31 A plane left Portland for Los Angeles at 10:08 a.m. The flight from Portland to Los Angeles took $2\frac{2}{3}$ h. What time did the plane arrive in Los Angeles?

32 Kumar used a bucket that can hold 5.5 L of water to pour water into an empty tank. He poured in 7 buckets of water. He then poured in an additional 3.5 L of water to fill the tank up completely. What is the capacity of the tank?

33 A blue ribbon is three times the length of a red ribbon. A yellow ribbon is $\frac{2}{3}$ the length of the blue ribbon. The red ribbon is 6.7 cm long. What is the total length of the blue and yellow ribbons altogether?

34 A square garden with an area of 36 m² is surrounded by a path. What is the total area of the path?

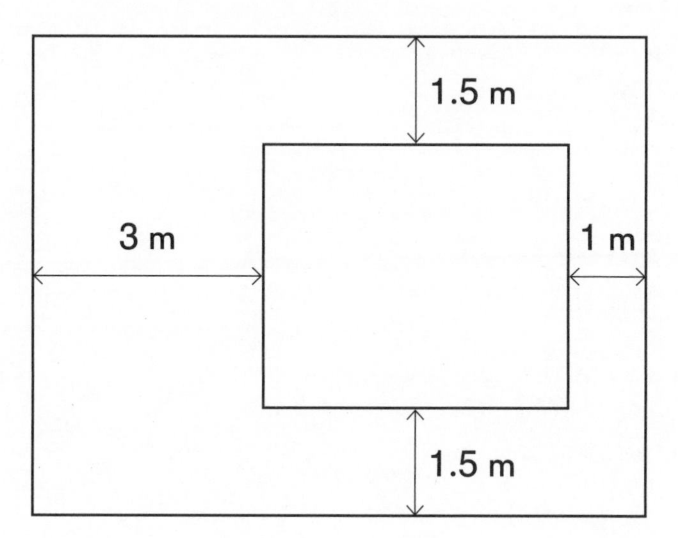

35. A notebook costs twice as much as a pen. A pencil costs $0.50 more than the pen. 2 pens, 1 notebook, and 1 pencil cost $7.00. How much does the pen cost?

60 min Score

Name: ______________________

Date: ______________________

Score
80

Test B

Year-end Assessment

Section A (2 points each)

Circle the correct option: **A**, **B**, **C**, or **D**.

You will need a set square, a protractor, and a ruler for this test.

1 Which of the following are common factors of 45 and 60?

A 3, 5, 15, and 20 **B** 1, 3, 9, and 12

C 1, 3, 12, and 15 **D** 1, 3, 5, and 15

2 What is the 3rd common multiple of 6 and 2?

A 18 **B** 12

C 6 **D** 30

3 Which of the following is a prime number?

A 81 **B** 123

C 109 **D** 77

4. What is the value of the digit in the tenths place in 158.09?

A 5

B 0

C 100

D 9

5. $\frac{26}{100}$ = ____________

A 2 tenths 6 hundredths

B 26 tenths

C 2 hundredths 6 tenths

D 2 tens 6 ones

6. 24 fl oz = [ ] pt

A 3

B 1.5

C 6

D 15

7. What is $\frac{29}{4}$ expressed as a decimal?

A 29.4

B 7.5

C 2.94

D 7.25

8. $1 - \frac{7}{100} =$ [ ]

A 3

B 0.03

C 0.3

D 0.93

9 What is 25 seconds as a fraction of 3 min in simplest form?

A $\frac{1}{12}$

B $\frac{3}{25}$

C $\frac{25}{180}$

D $\frac{5}{36}$

10 A rectangular picture is $2\frac{1}{2}$ ft long and 13 in wide. What is the perimeter of this picture in feet and inches?

A 7 ft 2 in

B 8 ft 6 in

C 32 ft 6 in

D 84 in

11 ABCD is a parallelogram. Which line is the same length as ED?

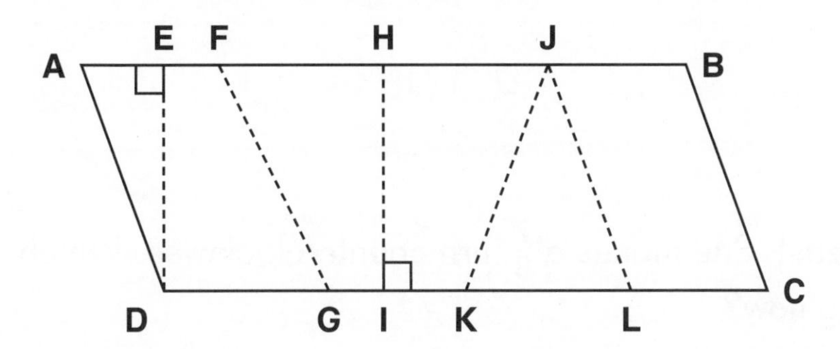

A JK

B HI

C JL

D AD

12 163.04 rounded to 1 decimal place is ☐.

A 163.1

B 163

C 163.0

D 16.3

13 480.08 ÷ 8 = ☐

A 56.3 **B** 60.01

C 53.65 **D** 66.35

14 ABCE is a rectangle. Find ∠DBC.

A B

49°

E D C

A 49° **B** 90°

C 41° **D** 131°

15 Sofia is facing southeast. She makes a $\frac{7}{8}$ turn counterclockwise. Which direction is she facing now?

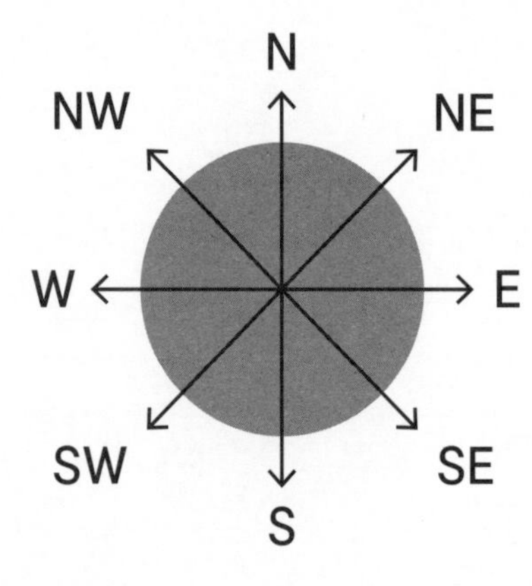

A NW **B** SW

C S **D** N

Section B (2 points each)

16. Use the digits 2, 4, 0, 9, and 3 to form the least 5-digit even number.

17. One bicycle costs $138.60. How much do 4 bicycles cost?

18. Write 3,407.69 in expanded form.

19. A basket of berries weighs $2\frac{1}{4}$ lb. The empty basket weighs 7 oz. How much do the berries weigh in pounds and ounces?

The line plot shows the number of pumpkins by weight to the nearest fourth of a pound sold by a farmer this morning.
Use the plot to answer questions 20–22.

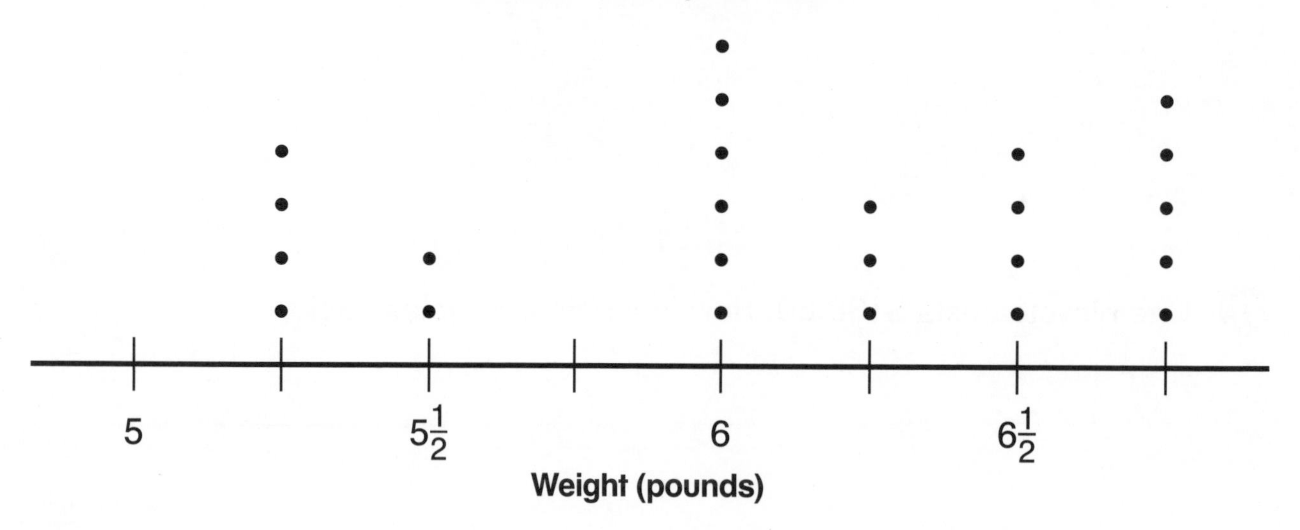

20 How many pumpkins sold were more than $5\frac{1}{2}$ lb?

21 The price of each pumpkin was \$6. How much did the farmer receive from selling pumpkins this morning?

22 What fraction of the total pumpkins sold weigh between 5 and $5\frac{3}{4}$ lb? Express the answer in simplest form.

23 Arrange the numbers from least to greatest.

$3.4, \frac{3}{4}, 0.43, \frac{4}{3}, 4.3$

______ ______ ______ ______ ______

24 Write >, <, or = in the ◯.

$0.08 + 5.2$ ◯ $6 - 0.72$

25 EG is a straight line. What is the measure of ∠HFI?

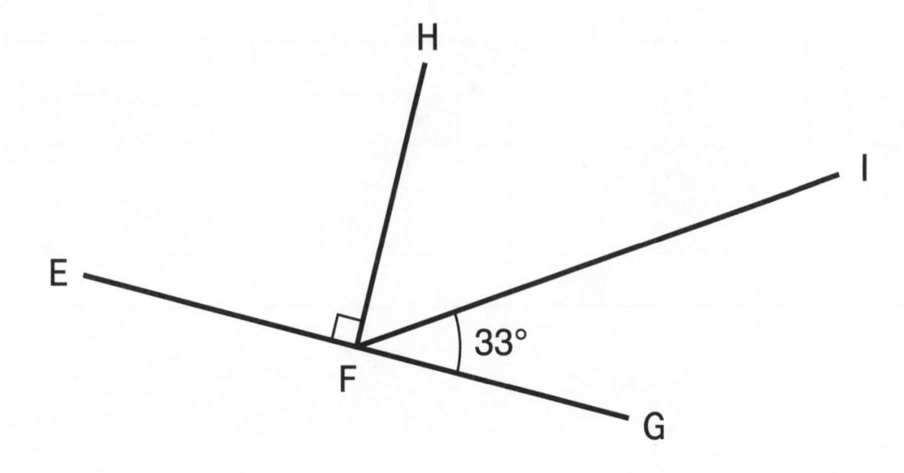

26 Name two pairs of perpendicular lines and two pairs of parallel lines in the diagram below.

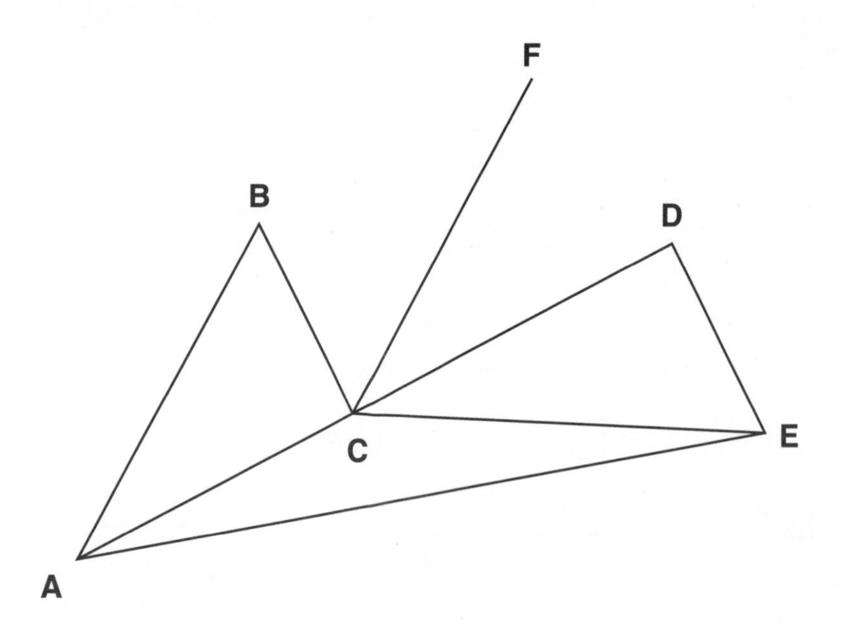

27 Which figures have 4 lines of symmetry?

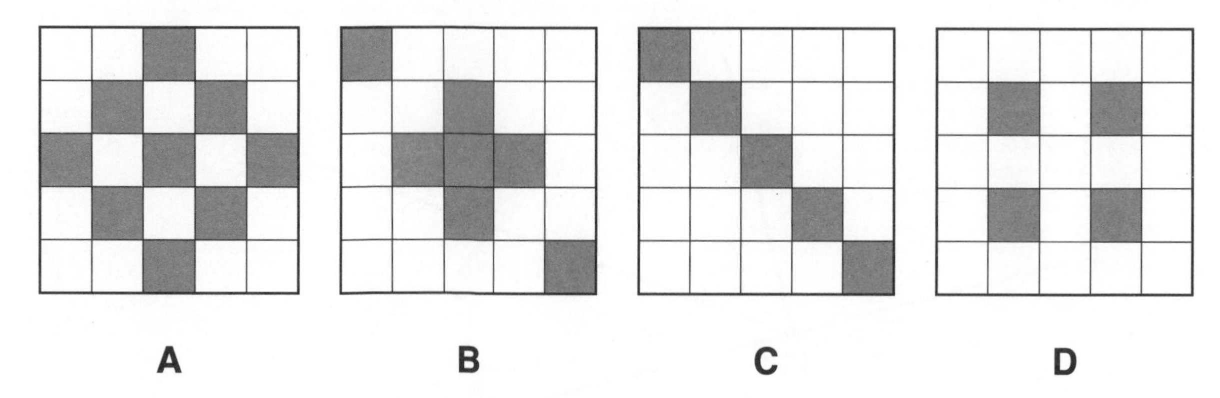

Use this cuboid to answer questions 28–30.

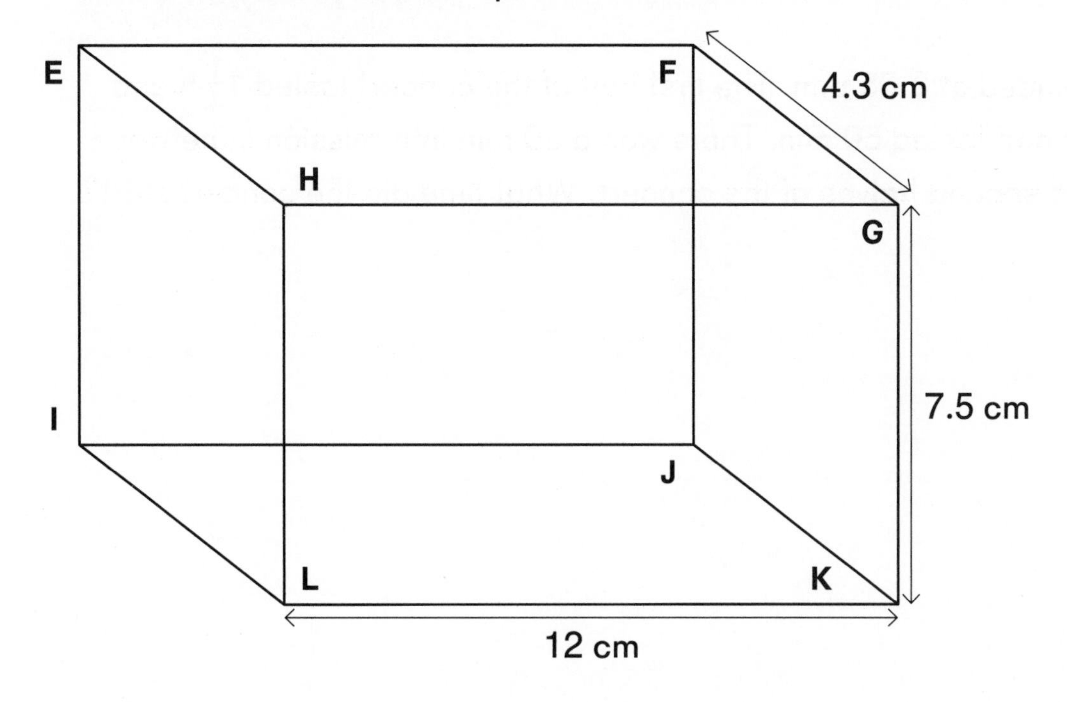

28 List two edges that are parallel to Edge IJ.

29 List all the faces that have an area of 51.6 cm². Use estimation.

30 What faces are perpendicular to Face FGKJ?

Section C (4 points each)

31. A concert ended at 2:05 p.m. The first half of the concert lasted $1\frac{1}{4}$ h and the second half lasted 50 min. There was a 20 min intermission in between the first and second halves of the concert. What time did the concert start?

32. Emma has a ribbon $6\frac{3}{4}$ ft long. She used 27 in of it. How much ribbon does she have left in feet and inches?

33 A rectangular portrait and a square mirror are hung on a wall with sides 7 m by 5 m. What area of the wall is not covered by the portrait and the mirror?

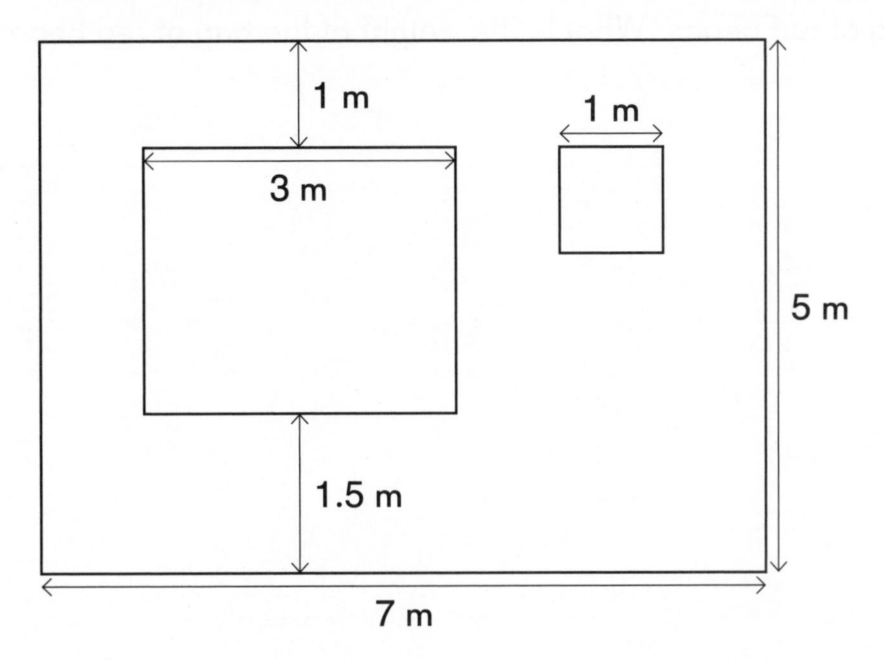

34 The capacity of Container A is half that of Container B. The capacity of Container C is twice that of Container B. The total capacity of the three containers is 59.5 L. What is the capacity of Container C?

A bag of red beans weighed 0.25 lb more than a bag of black beans. After 0.4 lb of black beans was used, the bag of black beans weighed half as much as the bag of red beans. What is the weight of the bag of red beans?

Answer Key

Detailed solutions given are suggestions, and do not include all possible methods of arriving at the correct answer. Accept all reasonable solutions by students.

Test A

Chapter 10 Measurement

1. C

2. A

3. C

4. B

5. D

6. 1 h 45 min

7. $\frac{80}{100} = \frac{8}{10} = \frac{4}{5}$

   $\frac{4}{5}$ m

8. 1 yd = 3 ft = 36 in

   $1\frac{1}{2}$ ft = 18 in

   3 ft 3 in = 39 in

   $1\frac{1}{2}$ ft, 35 in, 1 yd, 3 ft 3 in

9. 3 cm = 30 mm

   $\frac{1}{5} \times 10$ mm = 2 mm

   32

10. $1\frac{1}{2}$ h = 90 min

    $\frac{25}{90} = \frac{5}{18}$

    $\frac{5}{18}$ of $1\frac{1}{2}$ h

11. 6 kg 300g − 3 kg 340 g

    = 3 kg 300 g − 340 g

    = 3 kg − 40 g = 2 kg 960 g

    2 kg 960 g

12. 4 ft = 48 in

    $\frac{5}{6} \times 12$ in = 10 in

    58 in

13. 3×13 oz = 39 oz

    2 lb 7 oz

14. $55 \div 4 = 13$ R 3

    13 gal 3 qt

Chapter 10 Measurement

15 1 lb 9 oz + 5 lb 6 oz = 6 lb 15 oz
2 × 6 lb = 12 lb
2 × 15 oz = 30 oz = 1 lb 14 oz
13 lb 14 oz

---

16 1,300 mL − 800 mL = 500 mL
500 ÷ 2 = 250
250 mL

---

17 $\frac{1}{4}$ h = 15 min
11:55 a.m. + 1 h
⟶ 12:55 p.m.
12:55 p.m. + 15 min
⟶ 1:10 p.m.
1:10 p.m.

Test B

Chapter 10 Measurement

1. C

2. B

3. D

4. B

5. C

6. 1 kg 1 g = 1,001 g
   $1\frac{1}{4}$ kg = 1,250 g
   1 kg 50 g = 1,050 g
   $1\frac{1}{4}$ kg, 1,100 g, 1 kg 50 g, 1 kg 1 g

7. $\frac{4}{5} \times$ 1,000 mL = 800 mL
   $3 \times$ 800 mL = 2,400 mL
   2 L 400 mL

8. $\frac{1}{3}$ min = $\frac{1}{3} \times$ 60 s = 20 s
   15 min 20 s

9. $2\frac{1}{2}$ days = 48 h + 12 h = 60 h
   $\frac{12}{60} = \frac{1}{5}$
   $\frac{1}{5}$ of $2\frac{1}{2}$ days

10. 4 ft 4 in = 48 in + 4 in = 52 in
    52 in − 8 in = 44 in
    44 in = 3 ft 8 in
    3 ft 8 in

11. $\frac{3}{4}$ gal = $\frac{3}{4} \times$ 8 pt = 6 pt
    $2\frac{3}{4}$ gal = 22 pt
    22 pt − 7 pt = 15 pt
    15 pt

12. 3 m 15 cm − 95 cm
    = 3 m − 80 cm
    = 300 cm − 80 cm = 220 cm
    2 m 20 cm

13. 5:00 a.m. to 6:00 p.m. ⟶ 13 h
    $5 \times$ 13 h = 65 h
    65 h

14. $\frac{2}{5} \times$ 1,000 m = 400 m
    $1\frac{2}{5}$ km = 1,400 m
    $4 \times$ 1,400 m = 5,600 m
    5 km 600 m

Chapter 10 Measurement

15

3 lb 9 oz = 48 oz + 9 oz = 57 oz

$\frac{1}{8}$ × 16 oz = 2 oz

$2\frac{1}{8}$ lb = 32 oz + 2 oz = 34 oz

57 oz + 15 oz + 34 oz = 106 oz

106 ÷ 16 = 6 R 10

6 lb 10 oz

16

10:25 a.m. to 11:20 a.m.

⟶ 55 min

$\frac{1}{4}$ h = 15 min

55 min + 15 min = 1 h 10 min

10 min = $\frac{10}{60}$ h = $\frac{1}{6}$ h

$1\frac{1}{6}$ h

17

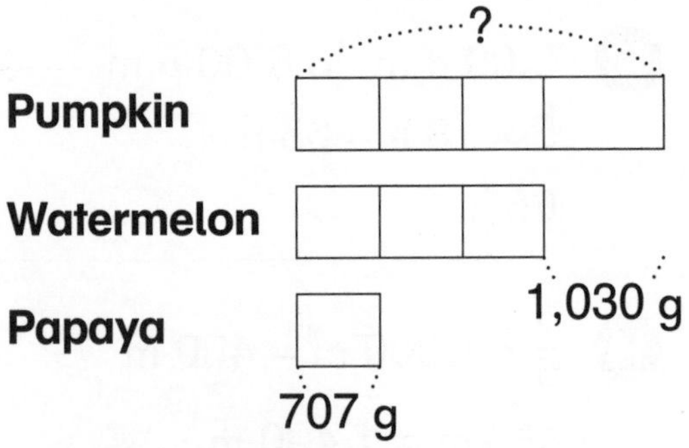

?

Pumpkin

Watermelon

Papaya

1,030 g

707 g

1 unit ⟶ 707 g

3 units ⟶ 3 × 707 g = 2,121 g

2,121 g + 1,030 g = 3,151 g

3 kg 151 g

Test A

Chapter 11 Area and Perimeter

1. B

2. C

3. A

4. D

5. C

6. $400 - 110 - 110 = 180$
   $180 \div 2 = 90$
   90 cm

7. 2 yd = 6 ft
   $168 \div 6 = 28$
   28 ft

8. 2 yd 1 ft = 7 ft
   49 ft^2

9. $12 \times 8 = 96$
   $20 \times 14 = 280$
   $280 - 96 = 184$
   184 cm^2

10. $3 + 4 + 5 = 12$
    $11 + 2 = 13$
    $12 + 12 + 13 + 13 = 50$
    50 in or 4 ft 2 in

11. $6 + 2 = 8$
    $8 + 8 + 7 + 7 + 4 + 4 = 38$
    38 m

12. 30 yd = 90 ft
    15 yd = 45 ft
    $92 + 45 + 92 + 45 = 274$
    $274 \times 3 = 822$
    $822

13. 1 km 500 m + 1 km 500 m = 3 km
    450 m + 450 m = 900 m
    3 km 900 m

Test B

Chapter 11 Area and Perimeter

1. A

2. C

3. B

4. B

5. C

6. $9 \times 4 = 36$
   36 cm

7. 2 yd 2 ft = 8 ft
   $96 \div 8 = 12$
   12 ft = 4 yd
   4 yd

8. $8 + 5 = 13$
   $12 + 5 = 17$
   $13 + 17 + 13 + 17 = 60$
   60 cm

9. $10 - 2 - 2 = 6$
   $6 \times 5 = 30$
   $6 \times 2 = 12$
   $12 \times 10 = 120$
   $120 - 30 - 12 = 78$
   78 in²

10. $20 + 20 + 15 + 15 + 8 + 8 + 7 + 7 = 100$
    100 in

11. 5 m 50 cm = 550 cm
    $550 - 80 - 80 = 390$
    $390 \div 2 = 195$
    195 cm = 1 m 95 cm
    1 m 95 cm

12. 1 ft 8 in = 20 in
    $20 \times 20 = 400$
    1 ft 8 in − 5 in − 5 in = 10 in
    $10 \times 10 = 100$
    $400 - 100 = 300$
    300 in²

13. $1{,}000 + 600 + 1{,}000 + 600 + 300 + 300 = 3{,}800$
    $3{,}800 \times 4 = 15{,}200$
    $15,200

Test A

Chapter 12 Decimals

1. B
2. D
3. C
4. C
5. B
6. 3.1
7. 10.8
8.

12.8	**12.9**	13
13.1	**13.2**	**13.3**

9. 10.13
10. 0.2
11. 6.04
12. 0.7
13. 3.2 cm
14. 9.0 (circled: $\frac{9}{10}$) 90 10.9 (circled: 0.9)
15. $10 + 2 + 0.3 + 0.04 = 12.34$

    12.34
16. $\frac{12}{100} = \frac{3}{25}$

    $\frac{3}{25}$
17. 1.6 m
18. 15.05, 15.12, $15\frac{1}{4}$, 15.27
19. $28
20. $1\frac{9}{20}$ m

Chapter 12 Decimals

1. D

2. C

3. B

4. C

5. B

6. 55.24

7. 40 + 1 + 0.07

8.

5.14	5.12	5.1
5.08	5.06	5.04

9. 67.91

10. 0.08

11. 501.04

12. 300 + 10 + 0.05 = 310.05
    310.05

13. $<$

14. 0.03

15. $\frac{9}{4} = 2\frac{1}{4}$
    $\frac{1}{4} = 0.25$
    2.25

16. $0.6 = \frac{6}{10} = \frac{3}{5}$
    $50\frac{3}{5}$

17. $3\frac{3}{4}$, 3.7, $2\frac{5}{10}$, 2.3

18. (a) $\frac{75}{100} = \frac{3}{4}$
    $10\frac{3}{4}$ kg
    (b) 10 kg 750 g

19. (a) 9.6 min
    (b) 10 min

20. $\frac{4}{5} = \frac{8}{10} = 0.8$
    0.8

Test A

Chapter 13 Addition and Subtraction of Decimals

1. A
2. D
3. B
4. C
5. C
6. 0.07
7. 0.9
8. $\frac{2}{5}$
9. 14.68
10. >
11. 8.73
12. 6.71 kg
13. 1.9 kg
14. 10.3 gal
15. $\frac{1}{4} = 0.25$

    $1 - 0.5 - 0.25 = 0.25$

    0.25 L
16. 4.63 lb
17. Alex: \$9.55; Mei: \$0.50 more; Emma: \$1.75 less; ?

    $9.55 + 0.50 = 10.05$

    $10.05 - 1.75 = 8.30$

    $9.55 + 10.05 + 8.30 = 27.90$

    \$27.90

Test B

Chapter 13 Addition and Subtraction of Decimals

1. B
2. A
3. D
4. C
5. B
6. 0.01
7. 0.01
8. 9.03
9. 10.73
10. | 11.8 | 11.64 | 11.48 |
    |---|---|---|
    | 11.32 | 11.16 | 11 |
11. <
12. 1.32 min
13. $7\frac{2}{5} = 7.4$
    $1.4 + 7.4 + 0.51 = 9.31$
    9.31 kg
14. $5.00 - 4.20 = 0.80$
    $\frac{80}{500} = \frac{4}{25}$
    $\frac{4}{25}$ of $5
15. $0.89 + 17.15 = 18.04$
    $18.04 - 3.66 = 14.38$
    $14.38
16. $0.75 + 0.75 + 0.5 + 0.5 = 2.5$
    2.5 m
17. $0.6 + 0.6 = 1.2$
    $3.9 - 1.2 = 2.7$
    2.7 mi

Continual Assessment 3

1. B
2. C
3. A
4. C
5. B
6. D
7. C
8. B
9. A
10. C
11. 500.57
12. 3 h = 180 min
    $\frac{30}{180} = \frac{1}{6}$
    $\frac{1}{6}$ of 3 h
13. 48 in = 4 ft
    36 in = 3 ft
    4 × 3 = 12
    12 ft^2
14.

97.04	97.06	97.08
97.1	97.12	97.14

15. 0.38
16. 6.69
17. 13 ft – 4 ft 5 in
    = 12 ft 12 in – 4 ft 5 in = 8 ft 7 in
    8 ft 7 in
18. 7 + 6 = 13
    17 + 13 + 17 + 13 = 60
    60 in

Continual Assessment 3

19 $60 - 15 - 15 = 30$
$35 - 5 - 5 = 25$
$30 \times 25 = 750$
$60 \times 35 = 2,100$
$2,100 - 750 = 1,350$
1,350 cm²

---

20 $1.75 + 7 = 8.75$
$36.25 - 8.75 = 27.50$
$27.50

---

21 $\frac{1}{4}$ h $= \frac{1}{4} \times 60$ min $= 15$ min
1 h 15 min + 5 min = 1 h 20 min
1:00 p.m. – 1 h ⟶ 12:00 p.m.
12:00 p.m. – 20 min
⟶ 11:40 a.m.
11:40 a.m.

---

22 5 lb – 2 lb 6 oz
= 4 lb 16 oz – 2 lb 6 oz
= 2 lb 10 oz
2 lb 10 oz ÷ 2 = 1 lb 5 oz
1 lb 5 oz

---

23 $\frac{2}{3}$ yd $= \frac{2}{3} \times 3$ ft $= 2$ ft
$3\frac{2}{3}$ yd = 11 ft
$11 \times 2 = 22$
$22 \times 11 = 242$
242 ft²

24
$1.15
Ruler
Notebook
Pen
?
$0.35

1 unit ⟶ 1.15
2 units ⟶ $1.15 + 1.15 = 2.30$
$2.30 - 0.35 = 1.95$
$1.95

---

25 $\frac{1}{2} = 0.5$
$0.5 + 1.3 = 1.8$
$3.25 - 1.8 = 1.45$
1.45 L

Test B

Continual Assessment 3

1. C

2. A

3. C

4. B

5. C

6. B

7. D

8. A

9. B

10. D

11. $700 + 10 + 5 + 0.4 + 0.03$

12. $1\frac{1}{2}$ m = 150 cm
$\frac{50}{150} = \frac{1}{3}$
$\frac{1}{3}$ of $1\frac{1}{2}$ m

13. $1\frac{1}{3}$ ft $= \frac{4}{3} \times 12$ in = 16 in
$16 \times 10 = 160$
160 in²

14. 0.04, $\frac{2}{5}$, 1.2, $1\frac{1}{4}$

15. 6.06

16. 11.92

17. 2 m 60 + 2 m 60 cm
= 4 m 120 cm
120 cm = 1 m 20 cm
4 m + 1 m 20 cm = 5 m 20 cm
5 m 20 cm

18. $5 + 3 + 5 + 2 = 15$
$20 + 20 + 15 + 15 + 7 + 7 = 84$
84 in

Test B

Continual Assessment 3

19 $90 - 30 - 20 = 40$

$70 \times 40 = 2,800$

1 m 10 cm = 110 cm

$110 \times 90 = 9,900$

$9,900 - 2,800 = 7,100$

7,100 cm^2

---

20 $2 - 1.53 = 0.47$

0.47 kg

21

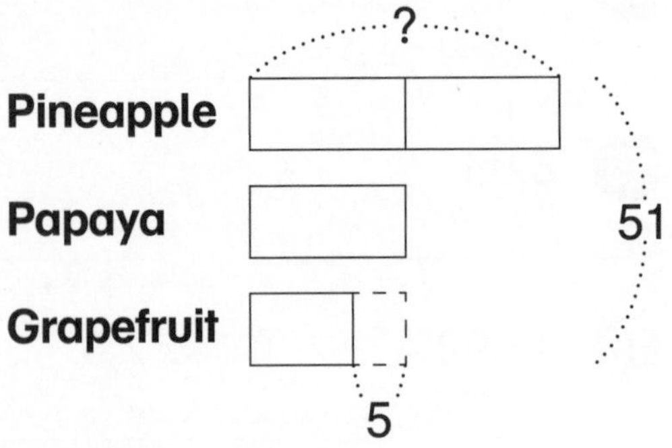

3 lb 3 oz = 51 oz

4 units ⟶ $51 + 5 = 56$

1 unit ⟶ $56 \div 4 = 14$

2 units ⟶ $14 \times 2 = 28$

28 oz = 1 lb 12 oz

1 lb 12 oz

---

22 7:35 a.m. to 2:10 p.m.

⟶ 6 h 35 min

$\frac{3}{4}$ h = 45 min

6 h + 35 min + 10 min + 45 min

= 6 h 90 min = 7 h 30 min

7 h 30 min

---

23 Width of window = 6 ft

Perimeter of window = $4 \times 6 = 24$

Length + width of door = 12 ft

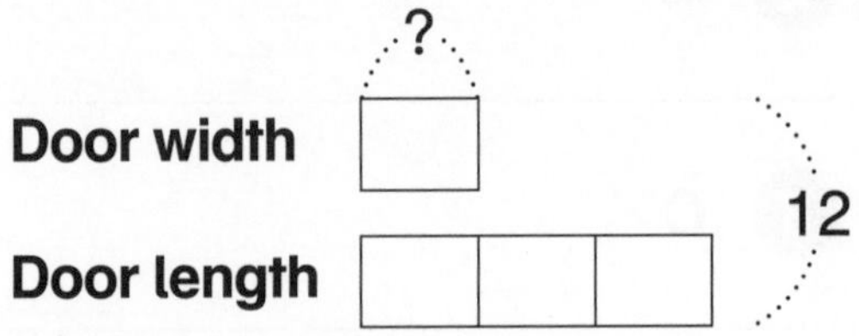

4 units ⟶ 12

1 unit ⟶ $12 \div 4 = 3$

3 units ⟶ $3 \times 3 = 9$

Door Area = $9 \times 3 = 27$

27 ft^2

---

24 $0.85 + 0.85 = 1.7$

$1.7 + 0.85 = 2.55$

$1\frac{1}{10} = 1.1$

$2.55 + 1.1 = 3.65$

3.65 L

---

25 $\frac{3}{8} \times 26 = 3 \times \frac{26}{8} = 3 \times \frac{13}{4}$

$= \frac{39}{4} = 9\frac{3}{4}$

$\frac{3}{4} = 0.75$

9.75 lb

Chapter 14 Multiplication and Division of Decimals

1. C

2. D

3. B

4. A

5. B

6. 0.25

7. 0.06

8. 40.04

9. 616

10. >

11. $4.6 \div 4 = 1.15$

    2 (1.05) 1.2 (1.12)

12. $0.5 \times 4 = 2.0$
    2 kg

13. $35 \div 4 = 8.75$
    $8.75

14. $0.76 \times 3 = 2.28$
    2.28 km

15. $3.60 \div 6 = 0.60$
    $0.60 \times 8 = 4.80$
    $4.80

16. $1 - 0.3 = 0.7$
    $0.7 \div 5 = 0.14$
    0.14 L

17. 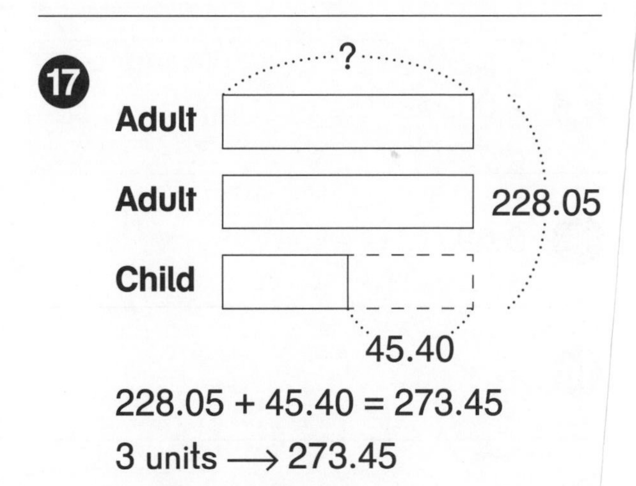

    $228.05 + 45.40 = 273.45$
    3 units ⟶ 273.45
    1 unit ⟶ 91.15
    $91.15

Chapter 14 Multiplication and Division of Decimals

1. D

2. B

3. A

4. C

5. B

6. 0.81

7. 0.08

8. 2,009

9. 0.09

10. >

11. $12.6 \div 4 = 3.15$
    3.2 is closer to 3.15 than 3.05.
    3.2

12. $25.50 \times 4 = 102$
    $102

13. $0.9 \times 8 = 7.2$
    7.2 L

14. $54 \div 8 = 6.75$
    6.75 miles

15. $2.5 \times 4 = 10$
    $10 \div 8 = 1.25$
    1.25 kg

16. $6.90 \div 6 = 1.15$
    $1.15 \times 8 = 9.20$
    $1.20 \div 3 = 0.40$
    $0.40 \times 5 = 2.00$
    $9.20 + 2.00 = 11.20$
    $11.20

17. 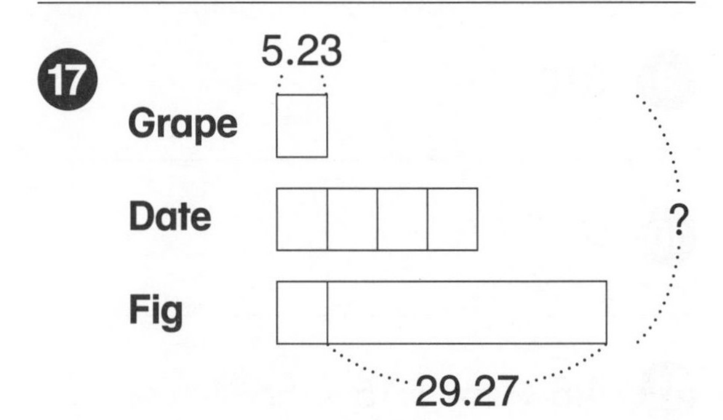

    $5.23 \times 6 = 31.38$
    $31.38 + 29.27 = 60.65$
    60.65 g

Test A

Chapter 15 Angles

1. B

2. C

3. A

4. B

5. D

6. 30°
   Measurement of angle may vary by a few degrees.

7. 125°
   Measurement of angle may vary by a few degrees.

8. ∠PQS or ∠SQP

9. 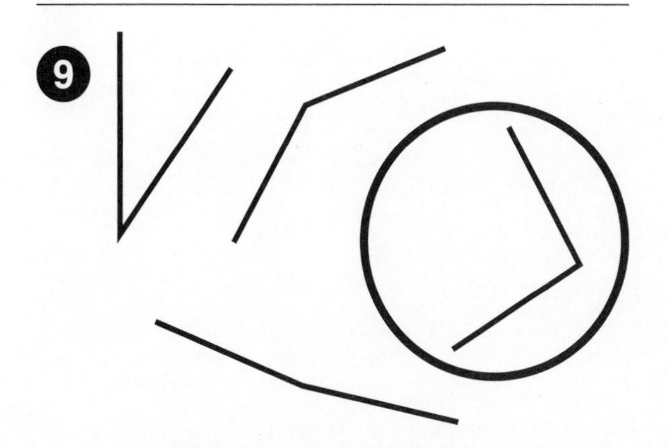

10. 86°

11. 152°

12. 340°

13. west

14. Orientation of angle may vary.

15. (a) Orientation of angle may vary.
    (b) 250°

Test B

Chapter 15 Angles

1. C

2. B

3. D

4. B

5. A

6. 60°
Measurement of angle may vary by a few degrees.

7. 175°
Measurement of angle may vary by a few degrees.

8. ∠KMN or ∠NMK

9. 21°

10. 61°

11. Orientation of angle may vary.

12. 80°

13.

An acute angle is between 0° and 90°.	✓
A reflex angle is smaller than a straight angle	
An obtuse angle is less than 90°.	
A full turn is equal to 360°.	✓

14. 205°
Measurement of angle may vary by a few degrees.

15. (a) Orientation of angle may vary.
(b) 285°

Test A

Chapter 16 Lines and Shapes

Order of letters for lines may vary throughout.

1. D

2. C

3. A

4. C

5. B

6. AB ⊥ AD, AB ⊥ BC

7. A, B, D

8. AB || GE, AG || BE, IC || HD

9. EF, IJ

10. C

B

A

11. 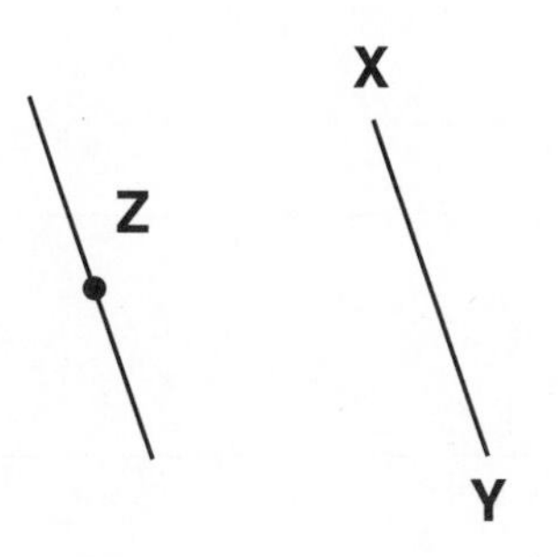

12. IJ || KL, EF || GH

13. 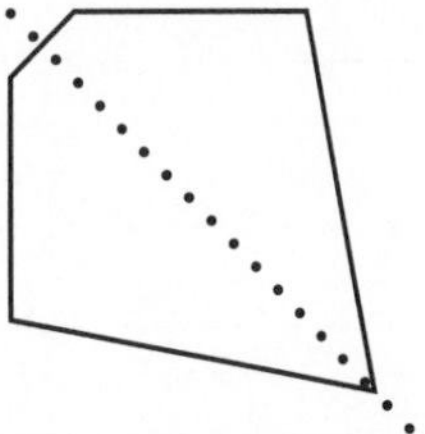

14. 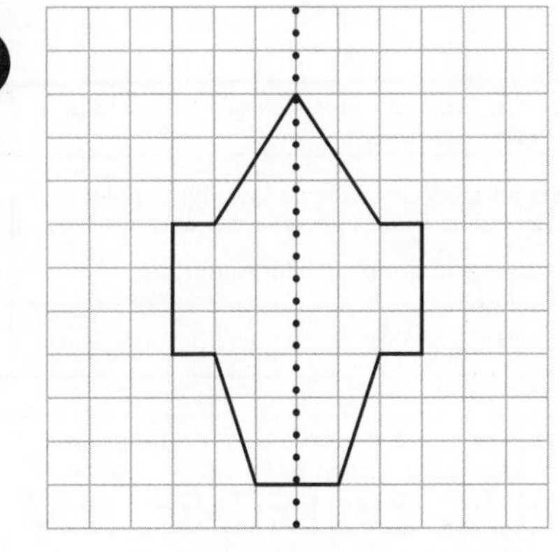

15. 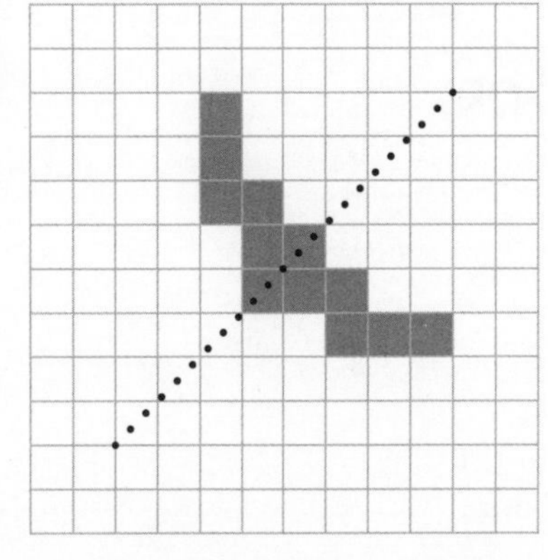

Test B

Chapter 16 Lines and Shapes

Order of letters for lines may vary throughout.

1. B

2. C

3. A

4. C

5. D

6. BA ⊥ AF, AF ⊥ FE, CD ⊥ DE

7.

Opposite sides of a parallelogram are equal in length.	
Some parallelograms have four right angles.	
All trapezoids are parallelograms.	X
A parallelogram has two pairs of parallel sides.	

8. AB || FC, FB || EC, FE || BC

9. KL, QR

10.

A

B

11. Line can be to the right or to the left of EF.

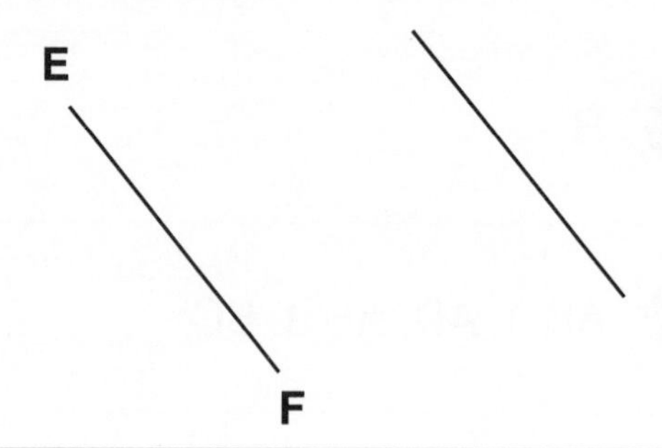

12.

A rhombus has two pairs of parallel sides.	✓
A rectangle has more than 2 pairs of perpendicular sides.	✓
All quadrilaterals have at least one pair of parallel sides.	
All parallelograms have at least one pair of perpendicular sides.	

13.

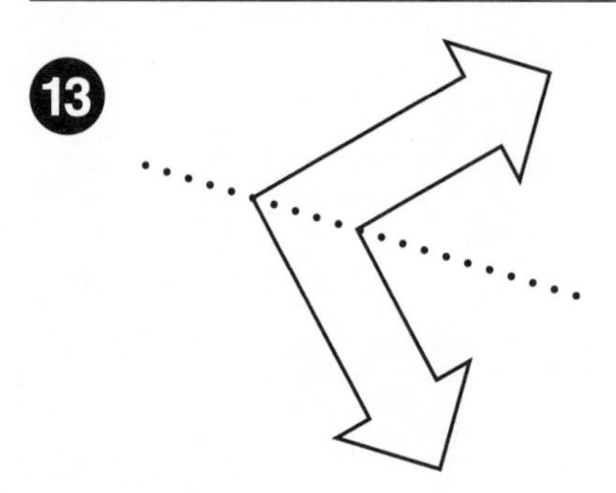

Chapter 16 Lines and Shapes

14

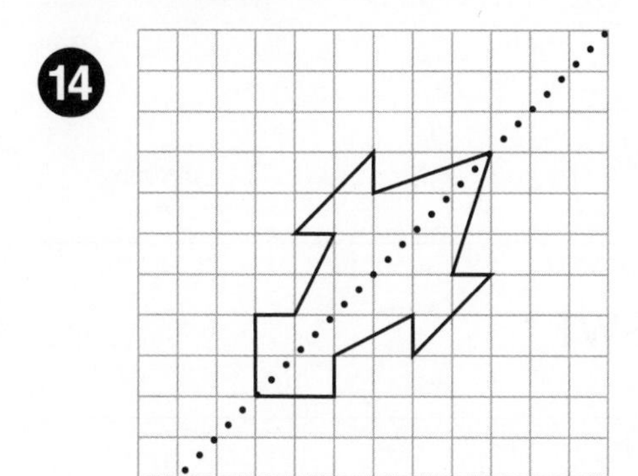

15

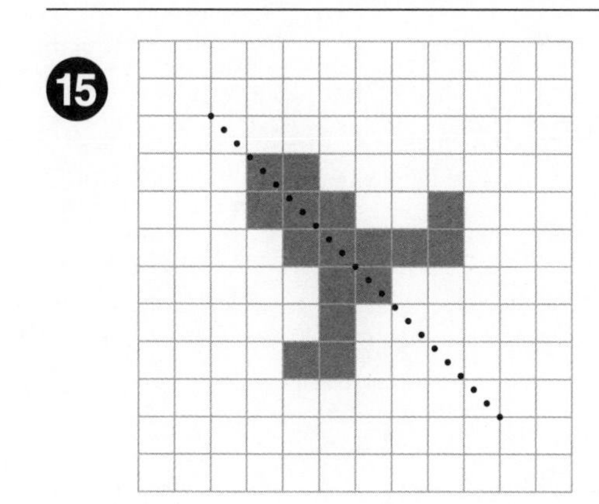

Test A

Chapter 17 Properties of Cuboids

Order of letters and names may vary throughout.

1. C
2. D
3. B
4. B
5. C
6. EI, HL, FJ, GK
7. EHLI
8. IJKL
9. $20 \times 15 = 300$
   300 cm^2
10. Any two: TW, QR, UV
11. SRVW
12. UV
13. PSWT
14. F
15. D and F

Test B

Chapter 17 Properties of Cuboids

Order of letters and names may vary throughout.

1. A
2. C
3. D
4. C
5. B
6. Any four: EF, HG, IJ, LK, EI, HL, FJ, GK
7. 32 + 16 = 48
   48 cm
8. 32 + 10 + 32 + 10 = 84
   84 cm
9. EHLI and FGKJ
10. Any three: TUQP, TUVW, WVRS, PQRS
11. TUQP and TWSP
12. TWSP and UVRQ
13. PQRS
14. FG
15. KLNM

Test A

Year-end Assessment

1. B
2. C
3. B
4. D
5. C
6. A
7. C
8. B
9. B
10. B
11. A
12. C
13. D
14. D
15. B
16. 50,000
17. 9.02
18. $50 + 2 + 0.1 + 0.05$
19. $5 \times 12 = 60$
    $\frac{3}{4}$ ft = 9 in
    $60 + 9 = 69$
    69 in
20. Wed and Thu
21. $16.50 \times 7 = 115.50$
    $115.50
22. $25 + 31 + 19 = 75$
    $\frac{25}{75} = \frac{1}{3}$
    $\frac{1}{3}$

Year-end Assessment

23. $\frac{2}{10}$, $\frac{7}{20}$, 0.72, 7.2

24. 3, 100

25. $7.2 \div 4 = 1.8$
1.8 cm

26. MS and PN, NO and RO,
NO and PO (accept any other correct pairs of lines)

27. 85°

28.

29. $20 \times 10 = 200$ cm²
200 cm²

30. Any two: KN, HI, GJ

31. $\frac{2}{3}$ h = 40 min
10:08 a.m. + 2 h ⟶ 12:08 p.m.
12:08 p.m. + 40 min ⟶ 12:48 p.m.
12:48 p.m.

32. $5.5 \times 7 = 38.5$
$38.5 + 3.5 = 42$
42 L

33. Red: 6.7
Blue
Yellow
?

1 unit ⟶ 6.7
5 units ⟶ $6.7 \times 5 = 33.5$
33.5 cm

34. $1.5 + 6 + 1.5 = 9$
$3 + 6 + 1 = 10$
$9 \times 10 = 90$
$90 - 36 = 54$
54 m²

35. ?
Pen
Notebook
Pencil
$7
$0.50

5 units ⟶ $7.00 − $0.50 = $6.50
1 unit ⟶ $6.50 ÷ 5 = $1.30
$1.30

Test B

Year-end Assessment

1. D
2. A
3. C
4. B
5. A
6. B
7. D
8. D
9. D
10. A
11. B
12. C
13. B
14. C
15. C
16. 20,394
17. $138.60 \times 4 = 554.40$
    $554.40
18. $3,000 + 400 + 7 + 0.6 + 0.09$
19. $\frac{1}{4}$ lb = 4 oz
    2 lb 4 oz – 7 oz =
    1 lb 16 oz – 3 oz = 1 lb 13 oz
    1 lb 13 oz
20. 18 pumpkins
21. $4 + 2 + 6 + 3 + 4 + 5 = 24$
    $24 \times 6 = 144$
    $144
22. $\frac{6}{24} = \frac{1}{4}$
    $\frac{1}{4}$

Year-end Assessment

23. $0.43, \frac{3}{4}, \frac{4}{3}, 3.4, 4.3$

24. =

25. $180° - 90° = 90°$
$90° - 33° = 57°$
57°

26. Any two: BC ⊥ CD, CD ⊥ DE, BC ⊥ AC, BC ⊥ AD, AD ⊥ DE
BA || CF, BC || DE

27. A and D

28. Any two: EF, LK, and HG

29. EFGH and IJKL

30. EFGH, HGKL, IJKL, EFJI

31. $1\frac{1}{4}$ h = 1 h 15 min
1 h 15 min + 45 min = 2 h
2 h + 5 min + 20 min = 2 h 25 min
2:05 p.m. – 2 h ⟶ 12:05 p.m.
12:05 p.m. – 25 min = 11:40 a.m.

OR

$1\frac{1}{4}$ h = 1 h 15 min
1 h 15 min + 50 min = 2 h 5 min
2 h 5 min + 20 min = 2 h 25 min
2:05 p.m. – 2 h ⟶ 12:05 p.m.
12:05 p.m. – 25 min = 11:40 a.m.

32. $\frac{3}{4}$ ft = 9 in
6 ft = 72 in
81 in – 27 in = 54 in
54 in = 4 ft 6 in
4 ft 6 in

33. $7 \times 5 = 35$
$5 - 1.5 - 1 = 2.5$
$3 \times 2.5 = 7.5$
$1 \times 1 = 1$
$35 - 7.5 - 1 = 26.5$
26.5 m²

34. **Container B**
Container A
Container C
59.5
?

7 units ⟶ 59.5
1 unit ⟶ 59.5 ÷ 7 = 8.5
4 units ⟶ 8.5 × 4 = 34
34 L

Year-end Assessment

35

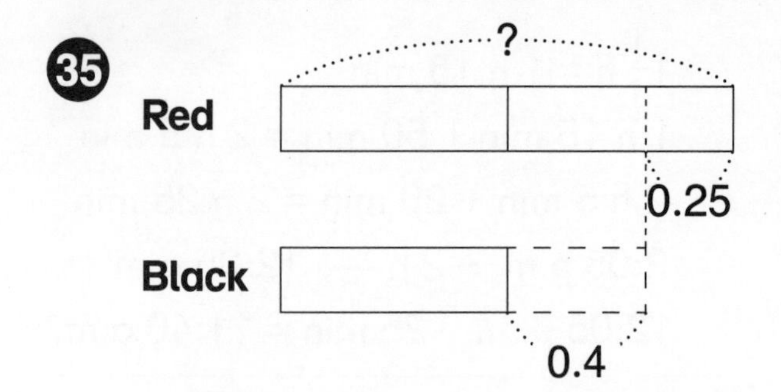

1 unit ⟶ 0.4 + 0.25 = 0.65

2 units ⟶ 0.65 × 2 = 1.3

1.3 lb